It couldn't be. . .could it?

'Jake. . .?'

'Hello, Annie.'

'What are you doing here?' she asked, her voice rough with shock.

'I thought you'd know all about it—Jo asked me.'

Jo—of course. She was always trying to get old friends together again—and Annie was always trying to avoid it. Until now she'd succeeded, but now Jake was here, churning up all the old, long-buried feelings that she'd hoped she'd forgotten.

'No hug for your old friend?' he said softly.

Dear Reader

Caroline Anderson gives us the final part of her trilogy, KNAVE OF HEARTS, where Anne meets her Jake again after eight years—a tearjerker! OUT OF PRACTICE is Lynne Collins's fortieth book for the medical series, and it is a lovely story set in general practice. I know you will enjoy it. Margaret O'Neill's hero, Rupert, is touchingly protective of Toni, and, to round off, Sheila Danton takes us to India, with all that country's problems and joys. See you next month. . .

The Editor

Caroline Anderson's nursing career was brought to an abrupt halt by a back injury, but her interest in medical things led her to work first as a medical secretary, and then, after completing her teacher training, as a lecturer in medical office practice to trainee medical secretaries. In addition to writing, she also runs her own business from her home in rural Suffolk, where she lives with her husband, two daughters, mother and dog.

Recent titles by the same author:

RAW DEAL
PLAYING THE JOKER

KNAVE OF HEARTS

BY
CAROLINE ANDERSON

MILLS & BOON LIMITED
ETON HOUSE   18–24 PARADISE ROAD
RICHMOND   SURREY   TW9 1SR

For Dee, who got me out of a corner! Thanks.

*First published in Great Britain 1993
by Mills & Boon Limited*

© Caroline Anderson 1993

*Australian copyright 1993
Philippine copyright 1993
This edition 1993*

ISBN 0 263 77996 3

*Set in 10 on 11½ pt Linotron Times
03-9302-52931*

*Typeset in Great Britain by Centracet, Cambridge
Made and printed in Great Britain*

CHAPTER ONE

WHAT a way to spend Valentine's Day, Anne thought wearily as she stripped off her gloves. The most romantic day of the year, and what am I doing? Inserting perineal sutures!

'Congratulations.' Smiling tiredly at the happy parents of a brand-new baby boy, she left them in the care of the midwife, her suturing finished.

It had been a tricky labour and she'd had to use Keilland's forceps to turn the baby before she could deliver him safely.

Theatre had been alerted, and the locum covering for Jo Carter, Anne's senior registrar and boss, had been contacted in case he was required.

In the event Anne had managed without any problems, and she imagined the locum had gone home.

She was wrong.

'The new guy's waiting for you in Sister's office,' one of the junior midwives told her.

'Lucky you,' her colleague said with a laugh. 'I wish he was waiting for me!'

Anne smiled wryly. 'Not another Casanova,' she sighed theatrically.

The nurses tittered.

'He's like a cross between Superman and Dirty Harry,' the second girl told her. 'Just point him in my direction if you've got no use for him!'

Just then Sister walked out of her office and the two trainee midwives snapped to attention and faded out of the corridor like magic.

'Ah, Dr Gabriel,' she said. 'All finished? Come and meet Dr Carter's locum. I have to go and see someone in the other delivery-room, but I think it's straight-forward. I'll call you if I need you.' She smiled con-spiratorially and lowered her voice. 'Take your time— I gather you're old friends.'

Anne frowned in puzzlement after the woman as she walked briskly down the corridor.

'Old friends?'

With a shake of her head, Anne walked through the door and stopped dead in her tracks.

It couldn't be. . .could it?

'Jake. . .?'

'Hello, Annie. Happy Valentine's Day.'

The man was lounging against the window, and as she stood there he shouldered himself away from the glass and moved towards her.

He was tallish, perhaps not quite six feet, but broad and well muscled, heavier than she remembered him but with the sleek heaviness of a big cat, all controlled power and rippling masculinity. His hair was dark, almost black, and fell forwards over his brow. It was shorter than it had been—it always used to fall over his eyes, but nearly eight years could bring a lot of changes.

There were other changes, too—lines around his eyes and mouth, not just the laughter lines that had always been there but the others that came with maturity, although in his case more likely just with age. His jaw was heavily shadowed but then it always was, even when he had just shaved. It was typical of his blatant sexuality that he had always needed to shave twice a day, she remembered with painful clarity.

He reached her then, his brooding, sensual face softened by a smile that cut deep grooves into his cheeks and set his eyes alight, those warm, deep brown eyes that could see right through you and could melt the deepest recesses of your heart—if you let them.

Annie had, once—long, long ago—but never again. She turned away.

'What are you doing here?' she asked, her voice rough with shock.

'I thought you'd know all about it—Jo asked me.'

Jo—of course. Jo had a thing about old friends, especially the ones who'd all lived together in their student days. She was always trying to get them together again—and Annie was always trying to avoid it. Until now she'd succeeded, but now—well, now Jake was here, just inches away from her, churning up all the old, long-buried feelings that she'd hoped she'd forgotten. Oh, God, don't let it be true, she prayed.

But it was true. She could feel him behind her, his body almost pulsating with life and vitality, coming off him like waves and lapping round her, unsettling all her carefully created status quo and seeping through the cracks in her defences. She almost laughed. Defences? Against Jake?

'No hug for your old friend?' he said softly, and suddenly there was a roaring in her ears as the waves came in over her head, swamping her.

The last thing she was aware of was the strength of his arms around her and the familiar scent of his aftershave, mingled with something elementally male and definitely Jake. With a soft sigh, she sagged against him and sank slowly into blackness.

His body was hard and strong and achingly familiar, and against her ear his heart beat steadily. Anne allowed herself a couple of seconds of self-indulgence before she opened her eyes and lifted her head from his chest.

'That was a very flattering welcome,' he said gently, his eyes smiling.

Annie struggled to sit up, but his arms were still holding her and he wouldn't let her go.

'Take it steady,' he cautioned, and then, releasing her, he eased her from his arms and stood up, leaving her on the big, soft chair in the corner of Sister's office.

'I'm tired,' she said defensively. 'I was up most of the night.'

'So I gather—you should have called for help.'

She laughed humourlessly. 'I'm an SHO—they're expendable. Anyway, I didn't know it was you.'

He met her eyes, and all the laughter was gone from his. 'Is seeing me again really such bad news?'

Annie looked down at her hands, then back at him, making herself meet those gentle, searching eyes. 'I'm not the person I was, Jake,' she said slowly. 'It's been nearly eight years—things are different now. We aren't at college any more, and I—I have responsibilities.'

'Your daughter—Jo tells me she's delightful.'

Anne looked away, unable suddenly to meet his eyes. 'Yes—yes, she's a real joy to me.'

Jake shifted, moving to the window to stare out at the light scattering of snow that blanketed the countryside behind the hospital.

'Why didn't you marry Duncan?' he asked, his voice carefully casual.

Her heart crashed against her ribs. 'I decided it wasn't fair,' she said carefully. 'I didn't love him the way I——' She stopped herself in the nick of time.

'The way you should?'

'Yes,' she agreed readily. 'And it seemed unfair to a

baby to have such a shaky start. My parents were very supportive.'

'I would have married you, Annie, even though she wasn't mine.'

She drew in a sharp breath. I must tell him, but not now, she thought frantically. Not here, in the hospital in front of anybody who walks in, and not now, out of the blue after all these years.

Sister popped her head round the door.

'Anne, I'm sorry to disturb you but we need your help for a forceps delivery. Would you mind?'

She stood up. 'Not at all, Sister. I'll come right away.'

She turned to Jake. 'Are you around later? There's a lot to tell you. How about this evening?'

He shook his head. 'I can't—I'm going down to my parents' to collect all my stuff. How about tomorrow evening?'

She thought quickly. 'Eight?' She could have Beth in bed by then. 'I'm only on duty until five tomorrow, then I hand over to the other team.'

'Fine. I'll see you at your place—that way you won't have to get a babysitter. What's the address?'

'Eight Bloomingdale Way,' she told him.

A slow smile spread over his face. 'Great. I'll see you then, if not before.'

It was a long day, and an even longer night. She snatched a couple of hours to go and see Beth, who was with her childminder for the weekend as usual when Anne was on call, but for the most part her mind was on Jake and how she was going to break the news.

She didn't see him again until Monday morning in the canteen, still in theatre greens and looking rumpled and deliciously sexy.

He came over and sat with her, and she noticed instantly that there were lines of strain around his eyes.

'Problems?' she asked quietly.

He shook his head. 'Not really. I've just done three terminations on the trot—God, I hate it. I thought I was finished with all that.'

He must be referring to his posh New York clinic, Annie thought without compassion. She knew abortions were an unpleasant but sometimes necessary part of Obs and Gynae, but actively to seek to make money from it seemed the height of obscenity.

'It keeps them away from the back streets,' she said now, and he laughed without humour.

'Oh, I know. There are pros and cons, and women in the middle fought over as if they were simply potting compost without any rights of their own, but I still hate doing it, and I hate myself for doing it, especially when it could so easily have been avoided by the simple expedient of birth control. God knows it's readily enough available over here.'

And it wasn't in the States? Annie stood up quickly before her tongue ran away with her. She really didn't need to get into an argument with Jake of all people about the availability of birth control!

'I have to go—don't forget tonight.'

He tipped back his head, his eyes curiously intense. 'When did I ever forget you, Annie?' he asked softly.

Anne walked away, her legs shaking slightly. When did he forget? He'd totally ignored her for the last seven and a half years, and he didn't even remember doing it!

It was a busy day, with several deliveries requiring her attention, but finally she got away and collected Beth from the childminder at five-thirty.

'Can I play in the snow?' she asked Anne.

'Darling, it's dark—and what about your homework?'

'It's only boring old reading, and I don't want to do it—I'll do it later.'

'You'll do it now,' Anne corrected firmly.

'No, I won't! Jenny doesn't make me! I hate you!' she sobbed, and ran from the room, slamming the door behind her.

Anne took a deep breath. Of course Beth didn't hate her, she was just crabby after the weekend. She hated her mother being on call, certainly, but she didn't hate her mother.

Holding that thought, Anne picked up Beth's rucksack of overnight clothes and teddies from the hall floor and followed the sound of her daughter's sobbing up the stairs.

She found her, face down on the bed, her tear-stained face buried in the pillow.

'Beth?' She perched on the edge of the bed and stretched out her hand, ruffling her daughter's thick, dark hair. 'Baby? Talk to me.'

'I hate you,' came the mumbled response.

Anne sighed. 'Did you miss me?'

'No.'

'I missed you. Did you play in the snow with Jenny's children?'

A sniff was followed by a nod.

'Did you build a snowman?'

Another nod.

She let her hand fall to Beth's shoulder and gave it a gentle squeeze. 'Why don't you tell me all about him while we have our supper? And then we can sit in the sitting-room and read your book together before you have your bath. OK?'

Beth sniffed hard, and rolled over.

'Can we have pizza?'

Anne groaned and rolled her eyes theatrically. 'Again?'

Beth giggled, her tears forgotten. 'Yes—I like pizza. Can I put the extra things on it?'

'Oh, darling, I haven't got any fresh vegetables and there's nothing much in the freezer.'

'Cheese?' Beth suggested hopefully.

'I think there might be some cheese. Shall we go and look?'

She stood up and held out her hand, and her daughter slid off the edge of the bed and slipped her little hand into Anne's.

Strange, Anne thought, how comforting another person's touch can be. They found cheese, and even a rather sorry tomato, and Beth decorated the frozen pizzas while Anne rummaged in the vegetable rack for edible potatoes. She had meant to go shopping, but Beth was so crabby and with Jake coming tonight. . .

She sighed and turned on the tap, and stood staring out over the little cul-de-sac. Light spilt brightly from the houses, and the street lights made gleaming pools of gold on the snow that had fallen on Saturday night. It looked enchanted, and a long way from reality, Anne thought drily.

She noticed that most of the drives were cleared, including hers—now which of her kind neighbours had done that for her? They'd even cleared the one next door, though that was pointless, because nobody lived there at the moment.

Several of the semi-detached houses, including Anne's and its partner, belonged to the hospital and were used primarily as family accommodation for doctors moving to the area, to give them a stop-gap dwelling until they found somewhere permanent to live. The hospital had agreed to let Anne's house to her for the duration of her SHO year in view of the fact that she had a child, and by an amazing stroke of luck the woman directly across the street from her, Jenny Harvey, was a registered childminder who had in the past looked after the children of hospital staff.

Not only was she very nice and extremely convenient, but she was also thoroughly familiar with hospital routine and quite happy to collect Beth from school with her own children and look after her at the weekend when necessary.

Anne would be lost without her, and she was well aware of that fact.

With another sigh, she picked up her vegetable knife and started peeling the rather ancient potatoes.

'How are you doing?' she asked Beth.

'OK—shall I put them under the grill?'

Anne turned and looked over her shoulder. 'Very pretty—put them on the grill pan, but let me light it.'

She dried her hands and struck a match, then fiddled with the temperamental grill until it lit with a great whoosh and settled down.

She put the pizzas under a low flame and turned back to the sink. She mustn't complain about the cooker. Really, they were lucky to have a roof over their heads, even if they did have to pay for it. The house was functional rather than cosy, but she had done her best in her limited spare time to bring an air of homeliness to it for Beth's sake, and they were very happy there.

It was their first home alone together, having lived previously with Anne's parents, and she was determined to make the best of it. Her parents had offered to continue to support her, but, apart from the need to be independent, once Beth had started at school Anne knew she would find time hanging heavily on her hands.

Her house year interrupted by her pregnancy, she had moved to Edinburgh to her parents' home and with their help had completed the second half of her house year in a local hospital before settling down to raising Beth. Now, Beth was older, and Anne had to make a life for them without help from other people. It wasn't just a case of pride, it was a fundamental need to survive out in the open away from the loving but often suffocating support of her parents.

They had moved from Edinburgh to Norwich a year ago, and when the job had come up only thirty miles from them, it had seemed too good to be true. She could have her independence, but she needn't be too isolated from them and Beth wouldn't lose touch with her grandparents. Sometimes, though, when the heating played up or the grill wouldn't light or the curtain tracks fell down, Anne wondered if it was all worth it.

Turning the temperamental grill down, she sliced the potatoes and par-boiled them before frying them in a little olive oil, telling herself that they weren't really chips and would be good for them, although God knew there couldn't have been much vitamin C left in the withered little offerings.

She really must get to the shops tomorrow. No wonder she had fainted in Jake's arms—it was just the combination of a hectic schedule and a lousy diet.

Beth had laid the table, the knives and forks the wrong way round, and Anne adjusted them quickly while she wasn't looking.

'Pizzas are done,' Beth announced from her station by the cooker, peering under the grill.

They ate their meagre meal quickly, and then, while the dishes soaked in the sink, they curled up together on the sofa in the little sitting-room that ran the full width of the back of the house, and Beth read her book to Anne.

The homework done, the snowman described in great detail and the tears apparently forgotten, they went upstairs and ran a bath.

While Beth splashed happily with her empty bottles and plastic toys, Anne unpacked the rucksack, hung up Beth's uniform and found her hot-water bottle.

The heating wasn't very efficient in the bedrooms, and as Anne tucked her daughter into bed a short while later, she reflected that all they needed to stretch her meagre resources to breaking point was a long, cold winter.

She had to pay Jenny, the rent, all her bills and feed them on a houseman's salary, and sometimes she wondered how they would get to the end of the month. At the beginning of the month she had bought an ancient and not very reliable little car, the best she could afford, so that they could go out on her few days off and have fun and to enable her to get to the hospital and back quickly to give her more time with Beth at the beginning and end of the day.

She would hate to sell it, but if it came to that she supposed she would have to. Such as it was, it was the only luxury she had left.

Kissing Beth goodnight, she made her way downstairs and quickly washed the dishes, then tidied up the sitting-room and ran upstairs again to change.

It was seven forty-five, so there was no time for a bath before Jake arrived. Knowing Jake, he wouldn't be late, so she wanted to be ready on time.

She opened her wardrobe doors and sighed. What could she wear? Not that it mattered, but she did want—— Silly girl. Why should it matter what impression she created? She tutted at herself, pulled a clean pair of jeans and an oversized sweater out of the drawer, and then sat down at the dressing-table and cleansed her face before reapplying her make-up.

She wore only the minimum for work, but tonight she stroked a soft, smoky green on to her lids to bring out the hazel of her eyes, and a touch of mascara to lengthen her lashes—not that she could hope to compete with Jake when it came to eyelashes.

A sudden thump from next door made her start. She glared accusingly at the dividing wall, then wiped the mascara off her cheek and peered out of the window. There was light spilling out on to the front garden, and a car on the drive—a BMW by the look of it. Must be a new consultant moved in over the weekend, she mused, and, on the way out of the room, looked at herself critically in the mirror.

Too short, too slight, her figure such as it was shot to bits by childbirth, her hair mousy, her face about as arresting as a blank wall—she turned away from the mirror in resignation, not seeing the gracefulness in her slender body, the appeal of her figure softened by maturity to a gentle womanliness, or the wistful, expressive quality of her large, green-gold eyes above her neat, delicate features framed by soft glossy hair the colour of polished hazelnuts.

Instead, convinced of her bland lack of appeal, she moved quietly through life, content to take a back seat and allow others to enjoy the limelight.

Sometimes she wondered sadly if that was all there was to be to life, but usually she was too busy to consider herself.

Tonight, though—tonight, she had to deal with Jake, and she needed a coat of armour to hide behind, never mind a dash of lipstick!

It was a few minutes before eight, and as she straightened the cushions in the sitting-room and turned up the control on the gas fire in a last vain attempt to make the bleak surroundings homely, she heard little footsteps on the stairs.

Oh, no, not now, she thought desperately.

'Mummy?'

'In here, darling.'

Beth's little face appeared round the door. 'I don't really hate you,' she said seriously.

'Oh, Beth, I know you don't!' Anne held out her arms to her small daughter, and hugged her tight.

'I missed you, Mummy.'

'I know—I missed you, too. Still, it won't be long before I don't have to work so many weekends, and then we can be together.'

'If it snows this weekend, can we build a snowman for my birthday?' Beth asked, her wide eyes doubtful.

'If it snows, then yes, of course. Now come on, you've got school tomorrow—run along up to bed, there's a good girl.'

Beth lifted up her face for a kiss, and blinked.

'You've got make-up on!'

Anne laughed a little awkwardly. 'I usually have make-up on.'

Beth shook her head. 'This is different make-up. You look—prettier.'

Anne blushed slightly.

'Thank you, darling.'

'Are you going out?'

She shook her head. 'No, I've got a friend coming to see me——'

'Is it Auntie Jo?'

'No, she's——'

'Auntie Maggie?'

'No, I——'

They both started slightly as a door slammed next door, and then seconds later their front doorbell rang.

'I'll get it!' Beth yelled.

'Beth, no!' Anne wailed, but the child was already down the hall, fumbling with the catch.

Perhaps it's the new next-door neighbours, Anne thought hopefully, but as the door swung open her worst fears were realised.

'Oh!' Beth said with characteristic lack of diplomacy as she eyed the big man lounging in the porch. 'Are you Mummy's friend? I thought you'd be a lady— Mummy doesn't have men friends.'

Jake grinned lazily and shouldered himself away from the wall, shooting Anne a teasing glance over the child's head. 'Doesn't she, now?'

'Not usually—come in, you'll let all the heat out and we can't afford to heat the garden,' Beth told him solemnly, parroting Anne's frequent plea.

He laughed, and Beth laughed too, her head tipped back, her face alive with humour, the thick black lashes framing the dark chocolate eyes that sparkled with mischief.

And then it happened.

Jake looked at Beth, then looked again, and emotions one after the other chased across his face. Disbelief, and incredulous joy, and a terrible, fierce anger.

'What's your name?' Beth asked him, her head cocked slightly to one side in a mannerism so familiar that Anne knew he would see it.

He looked across the child at her, his face still wearing a smile for Beth, but his eyes like cold steel, slashing through her.

'Yes, aren't you going to introduce me to your

daughter?' he said pointedly, only the slightest hint of a tremor betraying the emotions she could feel ripping through him.

She closed her eyes and counted to five.

'Darling, this is Mr Hunter. He's doing Auntie Jo's work while she's on holiday. Jake, this is—Elizabeth. We call her Beth.'

He held out his hand.

'How do you do, Beth?' he said gently, and a spasm crossed his face as Beth placed her hand trustingly in his and smiled.

'How do you do, Mr Hunter?' she echoed, and then giggled.

He almost glared at Anne above the slightly fixed smile. 'I think Mr Hunter's going a bit far, don't you? I tell you what, Beth.' He dropped to one knee conspiratorially. 'Why don't we make it Jake for now, eh? Since we're going to be neighbours as well?'

'Neighbours?' Anne croaked.

He straightened. 'Oh, yes. I'm going to be living in the house next door—won't that be cosy? We'll be able to get to know each other really well.'

Anne fled, almost dragging Beth with her up the stairs, aware with every step of Jake's eyes boring into her spine.

'We're going to make a snowman at the weekend— would you like to help?' Beth said over her shoulder.

'My pleasure.'

Anne tugged at the reluctant hand. 'Come on, young lady, it's way past your bedtime. Say goodnight.'

She spent as long as she dared tucking Beth up again, but finally she had no choice.

Her heart in her mouth, she made her way downstairs.

Jake was in the sitting-room on the sofa, Beth's latest

drawing in his hands, and as she watched he straightened up and glared at her accusingly, his eyes blazing
with anger and recrimination.

His voice was deadly quiet in the stillness.

'Why the hell didn't you tell me?'

CHAPTER TWO

ANNE'S legs were trembling, her whole body starting to shake with reaction. This wasn't the way she had wanted him to find out!

'I was going to tell you—tonight. That's why I asked you here, but——'

'Just tell me something—if we hadn't been thrown together like this, would you ever have told me?'

She looked away, unable to bear the anger and condemnation in his eyes.

'It isn't that simple, Jake——'

'Of course it is!' he growled. 'How much more bloody simple can it get? "You have a daughter". Four words. Is that really so hard?'

'Yes!' she cried. 'Yes, it is that hard! And what would you have done about it anyway? We were friends, Jake, just simply friends. That night was a fluke, a one-off. How could I hold you responsible? You made your feelings pretty clear, anyway. Your last words to me were, "This needn't make any difference to us, Annie. You're going to marry Duncan and I'm going to finish sowing my wild oats and see the world——"'

'But I said——'

'I know what you said. I know exactly what you said. We were who we were, Jake. It would never have worked.'

'You weren't even prepared to give it a try! Damn it, Annie, if I'd known she was mine——'

'What? What would you have done? For God's

21

sake, Hunter, you were a playboy, a womanising, hell-raising, over-sexed, overgrown adolescent! You weren't ready for the responsibility of parenthood, and I wasn't ready to risk my daughter's happiness—or mine—on a feckless, footloose itinerant!'

He snorted in disgust. 'Come on, Annie, that's a gross exaggeration——'

'No, it isn't! You were appalling—you had the morals of an alley-cat, Jacob Hunter! Every night there was a different victim——'

'Rubbish! You've forgotten——'

'Bull! I've forgotten nothing, Jake. Not one single, solitary damn second of that last year have I forgotten, and I certainly haven't forgotten the number of nights you never even made it home——!'

She broke off, appalled that she had revealed so much.

'Did you lie awake and wait for me, Annie?' he asked, and beneath the softly voiced sarcasm she thought she detected a certain wistfulness.

'Of course not,' she denied hotly. 'Why should I have lost sleep over you?'

He stared at her in silence for a moment, then looked away, his breath leaving his body in a sharp sigh. 'You think a lot of me, don't you?'

She slumped into a chair. 'I think a hell of a lot of you, Jake. I always have done, but that doesn't mean I've ever let it cloud my judgement. You were a good friend, the best, but you would have made a rotten husband and father seven years ago.'

'And now?'

'Now what?'

'What kind of a husband and father would I make now, Annie? Because you can be sure of one thing— I'm not letting her go. I don't want carefully measured visitation rights, or joint custody or some other legal arrangement. I want to be her father, in every sense of the word. I want a say in her upbringing and education, and I'm not convinced I want you out at work leaving her with a stranger for the weekend while you're on call!'

'Huh! And how the hell am I supposed to provide for her if I don't go out to work?'

'I'll provide for her—for both of you——'

'Over my dead body! And anyway, Jenny's a registered childminder, not a stranger——'

'She is to me. How do I know if I can trust her with my daughter?'

Anne glared at him. 'She's not your daughter, she's my daughter. I carried her, I gave birth to her, I've brought her up and cared for her and made all the decisions for her while you were off seeing the world and getting married——'

'You could have married me.'

'Oh, yes—we've been through all that. You weren't ready, Jake. Look what happened when you did get married.'

'There was no child involved.'

'Would it have made any difference?'

He met her eyes briefly, then looked away. 'Probably not.'

'You see? Just one more example of your feckless attitude to life, but Beth's one toy you're not going to pick up and drop—damn it, Jake, I nearly died giving birth to her! She's mine, and I'm not going to let you have her!'

Her emotions strung to fever pitch, she turned away to hide the sudden rush of tears that cascaded down her flushed cheeks.

Jake's hand, gentle on her shoulder, was nearly her undoing.

'I don't want to take her from you, Annie. I want to share her, get to know her. I want to love her, Annie, and I want her to love me, too. Don't shut me out. I've lost so much of her life already—let me share her with you. Please? Marry me now, Annie—make me part of your lives.'

Her breath caught in her throat. His touch was warm, undemanding, but she knew it could change like quicksilver to become sensual and erotic, giving and yet taking, demanding, searching. . . Dear God, what was she thinking? She was letting herself be swayed by the soft pleading in his voice, but she could never feel like that for Jake again, could never trust him——

'Marry you? Jake, are you mad? I wouldn't marry you if you were the last man on earth!'

He recoiled as if she'd struck him, walking swiftly away from her to stand broodingly at the patio doors, staring out at the dark, snow-covered garden. His hands were rammed in his pockets, his shoulders hunched defensively.

Immediately Anne regretted her impulsive outburst, but not the emotion that had triggered it. Yes, Jake was Beth's father, but that gave him no rights over her.

'You didn't feel that way about me once,' he reminded her.

'Yes, once and only once, and look where it got me!'

He turned and met her eyes challengingly. 'You could have had an abortion.'

'No!' She felt the heat drain out of her at his words. 'Oh, no. Jake, I loved you. You were the best friend I'd ever had. How could I have killed your child?'

As she watched, the challenging anger faded from

his eyes and they glazed with tears. 'Why didn't you tell me, Annie? I've missed so much. . .'

He bowed his head, and she watched in horror as a heavy tear slid down his cheek and splashed on to his sweatshirt, all the more shocking for being so unexpected.

She didn't even stop to think. Her arms were round him, his head against hers, offering him wordless comfort while he struggled against the roiling tumult of his emotions.

After a while he lifted his head and tilted her chin, staring down searchingly into her eyes. His lashes, impossibly long, were spiked with tears, but his eyes were clear now, his emotions firmly back in control although his voice was gruff.

'Thank you—for having her, for taking care of her, for not taking the easy way out.'

She shook her head. 'This was the easy way out— but not only that, for me it was the only way. Don't thank me. I didn't do it for you.'

'I'm thanking you for my daughter,' he reminded her softly, and then with a sigh he pulled her close again. 'You said you nearly died. . .'

She nodded. 'It was awful. Really she's lucky to be alive. She was an awkward presentation, and I just didn't have the pelvic capacity to cope with it.'

Jake led her to the sofa and sat, his arm still round her, while she told him about the fight to bring his daughter into the world.

'Why didn't they do a section?' he asked in bewilderment. 'Surely they could see you're too tiny to deliver anything but a straightforward presentation?'

She shrugged. 'It was a young doctor, and he kept saying she'd turn any minute. I knew he was wrong, I'd done my obstetrics, but you're very vulnerable lying there, and you don't feel like arguing. In the end I was too weak to argue, and then he called the consultant and they got her out in the nick of time. It's a miracle she isn't brain-damaged.'

'Don't,' he groaned, and hugged her hard against his side. 'Oh, Annie, love, I'm sorry. I should have been there.'

She laughed, a little shakily. 'I'm glad you weren't—you would have killed him!'

Jake chuckled. 'Probably.' He tipped her chin up with his fingers, and looked searchingly into her eyes. 'Poor darling,' he murmured, and then his mouth found hers, his lips soft and undemanding, his kiss a gift of devastating tenderness that brought a sigh to her lips.

Her body felt like liquid, melting against him as he deepened the kiss. She had missed him—oh, how she had missed him, but it had never been like this. Apart from that one wild, unforgettable night there had been only hugs and kisses of friendship, but this—there was something so right about it that it didn't occur to Anne to stop him.

Gradually the pressure increased as the kiss became more demanding, and Jake eased her down until she was stretched out on the sofa, his body pressing against hers so she could feel the hard imprint of his desire.

With a moan of frustration she arched against him, and he lifted his head and stared down at her, his eyes almost black with passion.

'What about Beth?' he asked, his voice roughened with need.

'What about her?' Annie asked absently, her eyes locked with his, drowning in the deep, peaty pools that mirrored her own desire.

He laughed softly. 'I'd hate her to come down and catch us—is there a lock on your bedroom door?'

'Bedroom?' she echoed stupidly, then suddenly reality came crashing back and she pushed ineffectually at Jake's solid chest.

'Dear God, what are we doing? Jake, let me up.'

He stared at her in disbelief for a second, and then with an untidy sigh he eased away from her and let her go.

She sprang off the sofa, her arms hugged around her waist, her whole body trembling. Dear heaven, what on earth was she thinking about to let things get so out of hand? And it wasn't as if she could avoid him—he'd made it perfectly clear he was going to be part of her life as long as Beth was at home. That meant ten or fifteen years of his constant presence, countless hours of discussion over Beth's upbringing and the direction of her life, and there was no way she could cope with that and an affair with Jake into the bargain.

Because that was all it would be. She knew him well enough to know that he was never satisfied for long with a woman, and that as soon as one had succumbed to his undoubted charm another would take her place.

No, life would be untidy enough without her own emotions torn to shreds by his devil-may-care attitude to sexual relationships.

'Come and sit down, Annie. I won't bite you.'

She laughed shakily. ''It's not your teeth I'm afraid of, Jake.'

'What is it, then? I won't hurt you, darling. Come here—I only want to talk.'

She hugged herself tighter and stared out of the window. 'You weren't talking just now.'

She could see him reflected in the glass, stretched out full length on the sofa, one arm bent, propping his head. He looked lazy and relaxed, like a big cat, and like a cat he was watching her steadily.

He came to his feet in one easy, graceful movement and came to stand behind her, his eyes never leaving the reflection of hers.

'What's the matter, Annie?'

She closed her eyes as he laid his hands on her shoulders and eased her back against him. 'Jake, we mustn't. . .'

'Why?' His voice was softly persuasive, his breath warm against her cheek. 'What harm can it do? I meant what I said, Annie. I want to marry you, and adopt my daughter, and look after you both.'

'No!' She pulled away from the warm haven of his arms and crossed the room, turning to face him like a cornered animal at bay. 'Jake, I meant what I said, too. I won't marry you——'

'You said you love me.'

'Loved—a long time ago, when I was just a foolish girl, but that girl's long gone, Jake. I'm a woman now, and I know what I want and need, and it isn't you.'

His brows quirked. 'Are you sure? That's not the message I was getting a few minutes ago.'

'Well, it's the message you're getting now, and that's the message you're going to continue to get.'

He laughed softly. 'Is that a challenge?'

'Challenge?' she scoffed. 'Jake, I live a celibate life. I wouldn't be much of a challenge to a man of your undoubted sexual prowess——'

'You're exaggerating again—flattering though it is, I ought to draw your attention to the fact that there have been precious few women in my life in recent years.'

She laughed. 'I'm sure it's like riding a bicycle, Jake, and let's face it, you devoted the majority of your youth to honing your skills in that department.'

'You're wrong, Annie, but I can't be bothered to argue.'

'Well, there's a relief!' She sat down in a chair and curled her feet defensively under her bottom. 'Look, I don't want to fight with you. We have to find some way of being together peaceably so that you can get to know Beth——'

'So you at least agree I should?'

She was shocked. 'Of course! I'd always intended to tell you about her, but somehow it never seemed the right time.'

He gave a soft grunt of laughter, and dropped back on to the sofa, sprawling out across it with one leg flung up on the cushions, one arm bent, head propped on his fist. His jeans, as always almost indecently tight, were stretched lovingly over his thighs, accentuating the power of his legs and blatantly outlining his masculinity.

She looked away.

'So where do we go from here, Annie?' he asked quietly. 'You seem to want to make the rules. What do you suggest?'

She shrugged, unsure of how to proceed. 'Play it by ear? You'll be living next door, so you should be able to have lots of casual chats with her and gradually make friends. Drop in for tea, invite us round for coffee, perhaps the odd walk at the weekend? She wants you to help her build the snowman, too.'

He was watching her again with that curiously intense look that was so unnerving.

'You are, I take it, including yourself in these arangements?'

'Of course—I have to, Jake! I can't just suddenly encourage her to spend hours with you without any reason. Normally I try and stop her from wearing out her welcome with friends, because she's very open and natural and can't imagine that anybody wouldn't want her.'

'I want her. Make no mistake about that, Annie.'

Her shoulders sagged. 'Just one thing, because remember I know you, Jacob Hunter. Don't encourage her affections and friendship and then decide paternity is too boring and fly off into the sunset. Do you understand? I don't care how you behave with your women, this is a different relationship, and, like it or not, it's for life. If you don't think you can hack it, then get out of our lives now. I won't have her hurt—is that clear?'

'As crystal.' He came fluidly to his feet and stood over her menacingly, his voice deathly quiet. 'There's one thing you should understand. I intend to be an active parent, Anne. She's my daughter and before long she's going to know she's my daughter——'

'No!'

'Yes. Oh, yes. I'm not having her calling me Mr Hunter or Uncle Jake. I want her to know who I am, and that I love her.'

'But you don't!'

'Because I've never had the chance, but that's all changed now, because you're going to give me that chance. I want to know everything—when she cut her first tooth, took her first step, said her first word—all of it, down to the last sleepless night, and you're going to tell me if I have to wring it out of you!'

'That won't be necessary. I have a book,' she told him quietly. 'I knew you would want to know one day, so I recorded everything meticulously. I'll get it for you. There are also videos of her as a toddler, and in the playgroup Christmas concert, and later in school plays and up at my parents' during holidays. Do you have a video player?'

He nodded. 'Yes, I brought it up last night.'

She rummaged in the cabinet under the television and brought out three video tapes, and then from the bookcase she produced a baby album and six other photo albums.

'One for every year,' she told him. 'The last one has a few more to go in it.'

'It must be her birthday soon, I suppose—God, I don't even know the date of my own daughter's birthday!' he said heavily.

'Sunday,' she told him, ignoring the anguish in his voice. 'The twenty-first of February.'

She produced a carrier bag from the kitchen and put all the tapes and albums in it.

'What have you told her about me?' he asked.

'I told her you'd gone away to America. By the time she was old enough to ask, you were married and in private practice, so we could hardly write to you and say, "There's something you ought to know".'

'And when you heard I was divorced?'

She shrugged. 'It just proved everything I'd always known about you and your relationships with women. I decided then that I didn't need the aggravation of telling you about Beth and having to deal with transatlantic flights and custody and access battles and all the other trauma. Frankly, Jake, we were better off without you.'

He glanced around at the meagre surroundings, and she felt his disdain for the marked walls, the threadbare carpet, the tatty old furniture.

'Pretty spartan, Annie. I wouldn't say you'd done that well.'

She was stung, her pride hurt. 'I've done my best, and there's more to life than money, Jake, odd though

you may find that coming hot-foot from the Big
Apple—or should I call it the Golden Nugget?'

He opened his mouth to argue, and then shut it with
a snap. Taking the carrier bag from her, he strode
down the hall and flung open the front door.

'I'll see you tomorrow.'

He stepped out into the night, and as she moved to
push the door to behind him, he slapped it back against
the wall and spun to face her.

'Incidentally, about that piece of scrap iron on the
drive. . .' he gritted furiously.

She frowned in confusion. 'Scrap iron? You mean
my car——?'

'Car?' he snorted. 'It's a wreck! The first thing I'm
doing is buying you a decent one, because there's no
way my daughter's riding round in that ancient death-
trap!'

Anne was furious. First the house, now the car!
'How dare you? Just where the hell do you get off
calling my car a death-trap?'

'Look at it! The thing's lethal—if it has an MOT
certificate I'd stake my life it's cooked. You've got no
business taking a child in a vehicle like that——'

'How dare you? It's none of your business what I do
with Beth——'

'Rubbish!' he roared. 'Of course it's my business!
She's my daughter, damn it!'

'No, she isn't!' Anne screamed, almost beyond
endurance. 'She's my daughter, and I won't have you
interfering—what are you doing?'

She ran after him, holding his arm as he wrenched
open the driver's door and pulled the bonnet catch.

'Jake, what the bloody hell do you think you're
playing at?'

'Disabling it is what I'm playing at. If you won't be

responsible, then I'll have to be responsible for you.'
He opened the bonnet, unclipped the distributor cap
and pocketed the rotor arm.

'Damn you, give that back!' she shouted.

'No.' He slammed the bonnet, and lights came on all
round the quiet little street.

'What's going on out there?' someone called.

'Damn it, Jake, give it back!' she pleaded.

'Anne, are you all right?'

That was Jenny's husband, out in the snow in dressing-gown and slippers with a torch in his hand.

'I'm fine, Phil. Just a silly joke. Sorry to disturb you,'
and then in an undertone, 'Jake, please, be
reasonable!'

'No. Evening!' he called to Phil, then, turning on his
heel, he scrunched over the snow to his front door.

'Goodnight, you little hell-cat. I'll give you a lift to
work in the morning. Be ready at eight.'

The door banged behind him, and Anne was left
standing foolishly in the front garden in bare feet,
suddenly desperately conscious of all the hidden eyes
watching her from round the street.

'Sure you're OK?' Phil asked from the safety of his
front door.

She nodded. 'I'm fine. Sorry!'

She closed the door behind her and sagged against
the wall.

What a scene! How was she going to face all those
people the next day? It was all right for Jake, he never
had cared what people thought of him, but she had to
live here and the way he was carrying on she wouldn't
be able to!

Oh, damn you, Hunter, she thought bitterly. Why
did you have to turn up and throw everything into
confusion?

She went into the sitting-room and warmed her feet in front of the fire, then straightened the cushions, made herself a cup of tea and took it up to bed, realising as she did so that she hadn't offered him so much as a glass of cold water in the three hours or so he had been there.

Sighing heavily, she prepared for bed, checked Beth and slipped between the cold sheets with a shudder.

She could have been warm, of course, if she'd let Jake stay—but what kind of an option was that? She punched the pillows into shape and sat up, cradling her tea in her hands and wondering how she was going to cope with having Jake as a next-door neighbour.

Not well, was the answer.

She could hear him moving about in the house, and after she had drunk her tea she lay down and tried to sleep, but her ears were straining for the sound of his movements on the other side of the wall.

After an age he came to bed, in the room that adjoined hers, his headboard against hers so that if she could have put her hand through the wall she could have touched him.

The thought unsettled her, and she turned over, punching her pillow viciously.

'Having trouble sleeping, Annie?' he asked mockingly. 'That's what comes of having secrets.'

Damn you, she thought heatedly, but her soft heart went out to him. He might be the most awful rake God ever frowned on, but she loved him, and just now he must be hurting.

'Goodnight, Jake,' she said quietly.

'Goodnight, Annie. See you in the morning. Oh, and Annie? Don't think you're going to win. I get what I want in the end, and make no mistake, I want you.'

* * *

'I want you'. Three simple words, yet they had the power to ruin her entire night's sleep!

It seemed she had hardly dozed off before she heard a knocking on the wall.

'Rise and shine, sweetheart—seven-thirty!'

'Go away,' she mumbled, and through the wall she heard his soft laughter.

'Not a morning person, are you, my darling?'

'I'm not your darling!' she said clearly, and, throwing back the bedclothes, she stumbled out into the frigid air.

Beth was still fast asleep, her dark lashes heavy on her softly flushed cheeks. Anne reached out a hand and stroked her hair back tenderly.

'Beth? Wake up, sleepyhead.'

The impossible lashes fluttered and lifted, and Beth smiled and stretched sleepily.

'Hello,' she said through a yawn, and Anne hugged her.

'Hello, darling. Time to get up now.'

She rummaged in the drawers for some clean underwear, and laid it on the bed with Beth's uniform. 'Here you are, darling. Get dressed quickly, there's a good girl, and I'll see what I can find for breakfast.'

Anne washed hastily in the chilly bathroom, scrubbed her teeth, and then rummaged for her own clothes.

It was time to get out the ancient twin-tub again and battle with the laundry, she thought with a sigh. There was no chance it would dry outside with the weather as cold as it was, which meant either a trip to the launderette or having everything hanging around the house on airers for days on end.

And there was no food in the house.

She went down to the kitchen and looked in the cupboards, like old Mother Hubbard.

Cereal, but not enough milk to go on it. Sunflower spread, but no bread. Porridge oats, but Beth wouldn't eat porridge without syrup, and guess what?

The doorbell pealed, shockingly loud in the stillness.

She heard Beth throw herself down the stairs.

'I'll get it!'

Anne shook her head and went out into the hall.

'Hi, Jake!' Beth said with a grin. 'Come in!'

He ruffled her hair, and looked over her head to Anne.

'Morning, ladies. I brought some hot doughnuts—I'm sure you hate them and would much rather have toast, but perhaps you'll help me eat them up?'

'Ye-es!' Beth positively bounced on the spot, her eyes alight.

Anne was irritated. 'I know I said invite yourself round,' she hissed while Beth was preoccupied with the baker's bag, 'but I never mentioned breakfast!'

'Seven,' Beth said, and then screwed up her face. 'Two each—who gets three?'

'I do,' Jake told her, and poked his tongue out.

'Don't teach her things like that,' Anne snapped.

Beth giggled. 'That's very rude, you shouldn't do it!'

He pretended to look chastened while Anne found three plates and set them down at the rickety table.

'Coffee?' he suggested.

'It'll have to be black. Beth, do you mind squash?'

She shook her head. 'Are we going shopping today? There's never any food here.'

Anne could have ground her teeth with annoyance.

'That's not strictly true,' she said defensively, but Jake leant back in his chair, sank his teeth right into the jammy middle of his doughnut and smiled with evident delight.

'I'll take you shopping,' he offered, and before she could stop herself Anne told him not to talk with his mouth full.

He choked with laughter, and Beth banged him on the back until he got his breath back and caught her wrists, tugging her on to his lap.

'Enough already!' he said, still laughing. 'You'll break my ribs!'

She giggled, reached across the table and picked up her doughnut, quite content to stay on his lap.

Over her head, Anne met his eyes, and the depth of emotion in them brought a lump to her throat.

She sipped her coffee and stole another glance. They were so alike! Not just in looks, although to see them together there was no mistaking their relationship, but in personality too. Fun-loving, with an overdeveloped sense of the ridiculous, always quick to laugh and ready to forgive—without Beth to take his place, Anne wondered how much more she would have missed him in the last seven years.

She stood up and cleared her throat. 'We ought to get on,' she said. 'It's almost time to drop Beth at Jenny's, and we have to be at the hospital soon.'

He left them then, and they had a last mad scramble round for satchel and reading book and gloves before they were ready to walk out of the door.

He was waiting for them, his breath misting on the cold air, lounging against his car in a thick leather jacket. Anne tugged her coat closer round her and forced a smile.

'I'll just drop Beth off with Jenny, and I'll be with you.'

'Hurry up, then, you're on the drag,' he pointed out needlessly.

She stifled her retort until she had delivered Beth safely across the road, fielded Jenny's intense curiosity and installed herself in the front of Jake's car beside him. Then she turned on him and pointed out with icy calm that it was he who had delayed them at breakfast, and if he hadn't stolen a piece of her car he wouldn't be obliged to give her a lift anyway!

He didn't bother to reply, concentrating instead on guiding the car over the icy roads.

It was only when he had parked and she got out rather too fast that she realised the road was just a sheet of ice.

'Are you all right?' he asked as she picked herself up.

'Fine. Do you mind if I don't thank you for the lift?'

He stifled the grin hastily. 'My pleasure,' he replied easily, and, taking her arm, he led her to the gritted path.

Once there and safe, she snatched her arm away ungraciously and, head up, marched to the entrance without looking back.

He followed her, his footsteps scrunching on the grit. They parted company at the entrance to the wards, he to Gynae, she to Obstetrics.

'Coffee later?'

'I should be so lucky,' she muttered.

He shrugged. 'OK. I'll see you.'

As it happened she did manage a coffee break, but, as luck would have it, so did Jake and they arrived together at the canteen.

'Wonders will never cease,' he said teasingly as he joined her in the queue. 'Two coffees, please.'

He paid for hers, dismissing her protest, and picked up both cups, scanning the room.

'Ah, there's Maggie—let's go and say hello.'

Anne was startled. 'How do you know Maggie?'

'Met her at Jo's.'

Did everybody but her know about Jake coming? She looked across the room at her friend, and then blinked. She was sitting on an armless easy chair, but not alone. A tall, blond man with drop-dead good looks was sharing it with her, his arm possessively round her shoulders, and they both looked like they'd won the pools.

'Hello, Maggie, nice to see you again,' Jake was saying, and pulled up two chairs. 'Is there a reason for the overcrowding?' he asked mildly, his eyes twinkling.

Maggie laughed, her soft pansy-blue eyes filled with happiness.

'We happen to like it,' her companion said with a wicked grin, and stuck out his hand. 'Ben Bradshaw, A and E.'

'Jake Hunter. . . I'm covering for Jo Harding— sorry, Carter. I've known her a long time; it'll take me a while to get used to the change. Jo and Annie and I go back—oh, eleven years?'

Annie nodded. 'Something like that.' She eyed Maggie and Ben suspiciously, but she had no intention of asking what she wanted to ask in public. The last time she'd seen Maggie, she'd been breaking her heart because Ben was getting married—in fact, he should have done so last Saturday, so why was Maggie sitting so close to him now that she was getting pressure sores?

Then she saw the ring.

'Catching flies?' Jake murmured, but she ignored him.

'Would someone care to tell me what's going on?' she asked.

Maggie tried to hide her smile. 'Fancy coming to a wedding on Saturday week?'

'But I thought. . .'

The smile broke out regardless. 'So did I, but I was wrong.'

Annie shook her head. 'Would you run that by me again?' she said plaintively.

Maggie laughed delightedly. 'You know I overheard Ben and Jan planning a wedding?'

'Yes?'

'Jan's his stepsister. She got married on Saturday.'

'But not to Ben?'

Maggie shook her head.

'So the ship's rat's not a rat at all?'

'Ship's rat?' Ben said indignantly.

Anne blushed. 'Sorry, just a figure of speech—Jo's, actually.'

Jake laughed. 'I'm not sure I quite understand what's going on, but do I take it that congratulations are in order?'

Ben chuckled. 'Yes, thank God. I never want to go through a time like that again. It took me five minutes to fall for her, and then another five weeks to persuade her to marry me—that's when I could finally get her to listen.'

Jake gave a wry snort of amusement. 'Is that all? You want to try courting Annie—after eleven years she still won't marry me, even though she knows how wonderfully easy I am to live with,' he said mournfully.

'You jest!' Anne retorted.

Maggie was wide-eyed. 'You lived with him?' she said incredulously.

'Not precisely,' Anne mumbled.

'Yes, you did—precisely. You just wouldn't marry me.'

She glared at Jake, and he shrugged and smiled.

Ben shook his head. 'Must be something wrong with your technique, old man.'

'After all the practice he got in? No chance,' Anne said drily, and then blushed furiously at the others' laughter.

She was rescued by the sudden bleeping of her pager.

'Saved by the bell,' Jake said with another chuckle, and, with a mumbled excuse, she fled.

CHAPTER THREE

'ROSS HAMILTON's wife Lizzi has just been admitted in early labour,' Sister told Anne as she arrived on the ward in answer to her summons. 'I've put her in the first single, next to my office. I wonder if you could clerk her for me, Anne?'

'Sure.'

She tapped on the door of the little room and entered, smiling a welcome to the slender but extremely pregnant woman perched on the bed.

'Hello, there. I'm Anne Gabriel, Alex Carter's SHO. I've just come to check you in.'

Lizzi smiled. 'Check away.'

'OK.' Anne ran through the list of questions, receiving prompt, precise and intelligent answers.

'You've done this before,' she accused with a laugh.

'Several times—I was a ward sister until maternity claimed me. That's how I met Ross.'

Recognition dawned. 'You were the ones with the cartoons—sorry, perhaps I shouldn't mention them.'

Lizzi laughed. 'They were only meant in fun. We collected them all and Ross had them framed for his study at home.'

Anne nodded as it came back. Apparently there had been a long series of hilarious cartoons following their budding romance, pinned on the bulletin board in the canteen, and by all accounts some of them had been pretty close to the knuckle. 'It was his registrar, wasn't it?'

'That's right—he's now doing freelance cartoons for

medical magazines, and earning a fortune, so he tells us. Never mind, we'll get our own back on him—he's doing Ross's list this afternoon!'

Anne laughed.

'Right, let's have a look at you and see how you're doing—have you had an internal yet?'

'No, we've only just arrived.'

Behind them the door opened and closed, and Anne glanced over her shoulder. A tall, good-looking man had come in, dressed in typical consultant's uniform of grey suit and sober tie, but most remarkable for the shock of prematurely silver hair above his lively grey-green eyes.

'I've sorted Mitch out for this afternoon. How're you doing?' he asked his wife, the soft Scots accent adding a gentle lilt to his concern.

'OK. This is Dr Gabriel—I think she's just going to do an internal. Are you staying or going?'

He laughed. 'Staying. I'm too old to shock!'

'Poor old man—what it is to be nearly forty,' Lizzi teased gently.

Anne hung the chart back on the end of the bed and smiled. 'OK, how frequent are the contractions?'

'Every twenty minutes or so? I had one just before you came in.'

'Still widely spaced, then. How about your waters? Have they broken yet?'

Lizzi spluttered and tried to hide her laughter.

Ross heaved a great sigh. 'I really think she hates my car. The first time she clapped eyes on it she rammed it in the side, and now this, the final indignity!'

Lizzi pretended to be wounded. 'I think your car hates me,' she countered. 'Every time I go near it it causes a row. Actually,' she told Anne with a twinkle, 'I think it's jealous of me.'

Ross snorted. 'I'm going to sell the damn thing and buy a Land Rover, I think. It's the only vehicle tough enough to withstand Lizzi's attention!'

Anne laughed, and turned back to Lizzi. 'Perhaps you could slip out of your clothes and put on a gown while I go and find a midwife, and then we'll give you a thorough check and see how you're getting on.'

She pulled a face. 'Do I have to wear a gown?'

'No, I don't suppose so. Do you have an alternative in mind?'

'I brought one of Ross's old shirts—Jo said something about the birthing-room, and I was hoping. . .'

'OK, that's fine. You can do whatever you want. This is your labour, after all. Just pop it on so we can have a look at you, and then you can have a shower. I'll just go and find your notes.'

She left them with a smile, and went back to the nursing station.

Opening the notes, she flicked through them, and groaned.

Under pelvic assessment, Jo had written, 'Possible disproportion—induce 40/40 latest, trial of labour—?android pelvis.'

So Jo had been worried enough not to want her to go past term, and by the sound of it she wasn't confident that Lizzi would deliver normally.

She decided to call Jake—at least in his posh New York practice he would have had plenty of experience with Caesarean sections!

She picked up the phone, called the switchboard and asked them to page Mr Hunter. Seconds later she heard the sound of a bleep on the ward, and Jake appeared at her side.

'Excuse me,' he murmured, and reached past her for the phone.

'It was me—I need you,' she told him.

'I never thought I'd hear you say that,' he said under his breath, and then told the switchboard operator that he'd been found while Anne dealt with the flush rising on her cheeks.

'So, what's the problem?' he asked, his eyes tracking laughingly over her still-pink face.

'Apart from your innuendoes?'

'I was only teasing.'

'And downstairs with Maggie and Ben? God knows what they think.'

He smiled wolfishly. 'They think we were lovers— which we were.'

'Once,' she retorted repressively. 'We have a patient. Consultant's wife, nursing sister—here are the notes. Looks like one for the big shots.'

He ran his eye over the notes and winced. 'Ouch. Rather her than me. OK, let's have a look. Have you examined her yet?'

Anne shook her head. 'I thought I'd check the notes first, but in any case I'd rather you handled it.'

'Chicken,' he said softly.

She shook her head. 'No, just deferring to your experience. I know my limitations.'

He snapped the notes shut and tucked them under his arm, and then, accompanied by the midwife who would be monitoring Lizzi during her labour, they went into the little side-ward.

Lizzi was sitting up cross-legged on the bed, dressed in a voluminous old cotton shirt with the sleeves rolled up and leg-warmers round her ankles. Her husband was perched on the edge of the bed, and they were laughing softly at something he had said.

Jake introduced himself, shook hands with both of them and then perched on the bed himself.

'Right,' he said to Lizzi, 'what did Jo Carter tell you?'

'That I might have problems and shouldn't go over term. Ross's other children by his first wife were fairly hefty, I gather.'

Jake nodded. 'OK. Well, as you must know, you're very slightly built, although you're tall, so before this goes any further we need to be fairly sure that you're going to be able to complete the delivery.'

Lizzi sighed. 'I had hoped it would be all right—in fact I'm not due for another twelve days. Jo even rang me at home and said she'd be back in time, and I'd be first on her list.'

Jake smiled. 'Well, you beat her to it, but it's probably just as well. The smaller the baby is, the easier it'll be, and it's plenty old enough now. This is your first, isn't it?'

She nodded.

'Is there a recent scan? I wonder if it would be a good idea to do one this morning if not.'

'I had one at thirty-six weeks.'

'Mmm.' Jake pursed his lips, thoughtfully, and then put down the notes with a decisive snap. 'Let's have a look first before we make any decisions—how are the contractions?'

'The last gap was ten minutes,' Ross said quietly.

Jake nodded. 'Good, they're picking up.' He washed his hands thoroughly, pulled on a pair of gloves and began to examine her.

'Well, your cervix is dilating nicely, about six centimetres, and the head's certainly well down. I just want you to relax as much as you can, Mrs Hamilton. I'm going to try and push the baby down to see how snug the fit is. It may be a little uncomfortable, but it shouldn't hurt.'

With one hand on the smooth curve of the baby's bottom, he pushed steadily down, his brow creased with concentration. After a few seconds, he released the pressure, straightened up and stripped off his gloves.

'Well,' he said, as he rewashed his hands, 'it's certainly going to be close, but the presentation is excellent, and I think you should manage it.' He dried his hands and smiled reassuringly at Lizzi. 'I'll order a scan now, just to be on the safe side, but I'm pretty confident you'll be all right.'

They left Lizzi with the midwife, and a few seconds later Ross followed them out.

'Could I have a word?' he asked Jake.

'Sure—let's have a cup of coffee. Coming, Annie?' They went into Sister's office, and Jake poured three cups of coffee from the jug in the corner.

'Ifs and buts?' Ross asked without preamble.

Jake shrugged expressively. 'Who can tell? Weak contractions, a shift in position? I honestly think she'll be OK, but she's going to need a lot of support.'

'You mean it'll hurt like hell?'

Jake smiled ruefully. 'She'll have a lot of bruising, and it'll be a long, hard second stage, but she'll still get over it much quicker that she would a section.'

Ross laughed uneasily. 'I don't know—I'm a surgeon, I'd far rather see a good, clean incision and rapid healing than all this horrendous wrenching and crushing of tissues.'

Jake chuckled and laid a reassuring hand on his shoulder. 'The female body is designed for it, you know, and it's not as if we haven't got the back-up. If she really can't cope, we've always got the option.'

'Can she have an epidural?'

Jake sighed heavily. 'I'd rather not. I know it sounds

sadistic, but it does tend to weaken the contractions and she's going to need good, strong contractions to mould the baby's head. Also, the diameter of the pelvis is greatly increased in a squatting position, so if things are tight that can make all the difference. If she's had an epidural, she can't get up.'

Ross shuddered. 'I don't know how you do it,' he muttered. 'I like my patients unconscious and oblivious!'

'She won't even remember it tomorrow,' Jake assured him.

Anne stayed silent, her heart going out to the woman in the side-ward who faced such a gruelling ordeal. It was easy for Jake to utter platitudes, he hadn't been through it, but Anne knew she would remember it, all of it, and she would need all the support she could get.

'I think I'll go and do my list and leave you lot to it,' Ross was saying.

'No!' Anne said, more sharply than she'd intended.

'Hey, I was joking,' he said, his eyes troubled. 'I'd never leave her at a time like this.'

'I'm glad,' Anne told him, her voice gentler now, 'because she's going to need all the love and support you can give her.'

Ross stood up and put his cup down, his coffee barely touched. 'I'll go back to her now,' he said gruffly, and left them.

Anne sat in the big comfy chair and stared accusingly at Jake. 'How could you tell him she won't remember it tomorrow? It's a lie, Jake.'

He came over and crouched at her feet, his hand on her knee. 'Annie, it won't be like your labour. OK, she'll have to work hard, but there won't be the difficulties you had with malpresentation, and, perhaps more importantly, she'll have her husband there to help her through it, and competent medical attention so that if anything goes wrong it can be dealt with immediately.'

He took her hand and squeezed it gently. 'Trust me, Annie. I'm not inhuman. If I feel she can't cope, I'll do a section, but it's much better for her to deliver naturally if possible. We'll decide after the scan.'

He stood up. 'I have to go and get on with my clinic. Could you book the scan, and call me when you get the result?'

She nodded and unfolded herself from the chair.

'I just hope you know what you're doing,' she said heavily.

'Of course I do—there's nothing wrong with my technique, remember?'

With a wicked chuckle, he opened the door and strode briskly down the corridor, whistling softly.

Lizzi's labour progressed slowly but steadily. The scan showed the baby to be if anything slightly on the small side for thirty-eight weeks, and so Jake decided to let her proceed.

They moved her to the birthing-room, and to the soft strains of a piano concerto her cervix gradually dilated.

Jake popped back every now and again, and Anne, although busy with other patients, was never far away.

'This room was Jo's idea, wasn't it?' he asked Anne when he came up during the afternoon.

She nodded. 'Yes—she had to fight Owen Davies for it, but she got it in the end. It's not much, and we've only got the one room, but it's been very popular.'

'I can imagine.' He laughed wryly. 'It's no comparison to the conditions I've been working in, but babies seem to get born no matter what.'

Anne resented his criticism, even though she knew the health service was badly stretched. All right, so it didn't have the facilities of his fancy New York clinic, but it didn't have the funding, either.

'We're very grateful for it,' she said a trifle sharply, and he raised an eyebrow at her tone.

'Don't get huffy, I wasn't criticising. It's hardly our fault that the best that technology and research can produce isn't available to everyone. How's Lizzi doing?'

'Steadily—her cervix is almost completely dilated now, so I guess we're about to find out.'

'Mmm.' He chewed his lip thoughtfully. 'I'd better hang around. The trouble with an android pelvis is that the outlet narrows the further down you come, so although you might get most of the way, you can get an obstructed labour right at the end, and then all hell breaks loose.'

'What do you do then?' Anne asked, appalled.

'Sever the pubic symphysis—the join at the front of the pelvis. That usually gives enough extra capacity to complete the delivery, and it heals quickly, but it can cause damage to the underlying tissues because of the sudden stretch.'

Anne shuddered. 'You're winding me up!'

Jaked laughed softly. 'It won't come to that, take my word for it. I've only ever had to do it once, and the woman had rickets. Let's go and have a look.'

They entered the dimly lit room, where Lizzi was lying on her side on the bed, Ross perched behind her rubbing her back rhythmically. They had put a clip on the baby's head, attached to the foetal heart monitor, and it was blipping steadily at a hundred and thirty beats a minute.

The midwife looked up and smiled at them as they came in.

'Hello. She's doing really well, just about to go into the second stage, and the babe's fine,' she volunteered, and then Lizzi lifted her head.

'I want to push,' she said firmly.

'OK, let's get her up,' Jake said decisively.

'No,' she protested. 'Let me lie here.'

'Lizzi-love, do as he says, you'll be better,' Ross said persuasively, but she was adamant.

'I'm not getting up—go away, all of you! Stop interfering!'

Jake smiled. 'Come on, Ross, help me get her to her knees.'

'No,' she moaned, but they positioned themselves at each side of her and lifted her into a kneeling position, still protesting.

'Just get it out!' she muttered through gritted teeth. 'I just feel so crowded inside. Let me lie down. . .'

'No,' Jake said quietly. 'If we can keep her upright, either squatting or kneeling, she'll increase the capacity of her pelvis by enough to make all the difference.'

'What do you want me to do?' Ross asked.

Jake grinned. 'Just make sure she doesn't fall over. We'll do the rest. OK, Lizzi, just lean on Ross—that's fine. Is that better?'

She nodded, and Jake moved out of the way and Ross took his position, sitting in front of Lizzi while she balanced her weight on him, her arms round his shoulders.

With the next contraction she tried to lie down again, but Ross and Jake persisted, and with the next one she actively began to co-operate.

'I want to get up!' she told them, considerably agitated, and they helped her into a squatting position.

'She's not going to have a problem,' Jake said confidently to Ross. 'Lots of good, strong pushes, but we'll make it.'

Forty minutes later Anne was less confident. Every contraction seemed unbearably long, and Lizzi was hanging on Ross, shaking uncontrollably and sobbing.

'I can't,' she wept, 'Ross, please, don't make me—I can't. . .'

Ross met their eyes, his face distraught, but Jake was determined.

'She'll be fine,' he said confidently, for the hundredth time, and then the foetal heart monitor started to beep a warning.

'Heartbeat's dropped to seventy,' the midwife said calmly.

'Come on, Lizzi,' Jake ordered. 'Stop fiddling about and push!'

'I can't!' she wailed.

'Yes, you can—now do it!'

'No!'

He took her by the shoulders and shook her gently. 'Lizzi, if you don't get that baby out now, it's going to die! Now shut up and push!'

'For God's sake, man,' Ross began, but Jake's warning head-shake silenced him.

'Heartbeat's down to sixty,' the midwife said.

'I hate you!' Lizzi sobbed.

'Fine! That's OK with me—just get that baby out. Right, here's a contraction—now! Come on! Good girl—and again! That's lovely. The head's nearly crowning—OK, one last push, gently now. Ross, hold her steady, she's nearly there.'

The midwife propped her back, Ross held her hard

against his chest, and as Jake told her to pant, the baby slithered into the world.

Ross eased Lizzi down on to the bed and Jake bent over the baby, his stethoscope on her chest while the midwife sucked her out to remove the mucus from her air passages.

'Call a paediatrician,' Jake instructed.

'She's on her way,' the midwife told him.

Despite their efforts, the baby lay unmoving, dark purple, silent, while Ross and Lizzi looked on anxiously. Jake shook his head.

'Oh, no, you don't. Cry, damn it,' he said angrily. 'Come on, sweetheart—one good yell.'

He flicked the soles of her feet again hard with his finger, and suddenly she bent up her legs and drew a shuddering breath. Immediately her body flooded bright pink, and she screwed up her tiny face and let out a bellow of rage.

Jake laughed with relief, and, lifting the baby, he laid her tenderly at Lizzi's breast.

'You've got a lovely daughter—well done,' he said gently. 'I think she's going to be fine.'

Lizzi reached out her hands and laid them on her tiny child.

'You've got your little girl, Ross,' she said with a faint smile, and Ross's face crumpled.

Anne turned away, her knees like jelly.

'OK?' Jake asked her gently.

'Yes—no—I don't know. That was so close.'

Jake shrugged. 'I knew she could do it.'

Anne sniffed, suddenly conscious of the tears on her cheeks.

'Too close to home?' he said with gentle understanding.

She nodded. 'Beth nearly died, too. She was flat like

that—she looked just the same, her nose all
squashed—oh, God. . .'

Just then the door opened and Maggie Wells came
in.

'Baby for me?'

Jake smiled. 'I think not, not this time, but perhaps
you could just check her over?'

Anne looked round. Lizzi was propped up on Ross's
chest, her face wreathed in exhausted smiles, the baby,
quiet now, staring up at her with rapt attention.

The cord had stopped pulsating, so the midwife
clamped and cut it, and reluctantly Lizzi released her
daughter to Maggie.

'I won't take her far,' she said smilingly, and laid her
in a perspex cot beside the bed, so that the proud and
somewhat disbelieving parents could watch as she
examined their precious bundle.

As she did so, the midwife asked Lizzi to push one
last time and delivered the placenta, beautifully intact
and without the benefit of oxytocin, which they no
longer used routinely on Alex Carter's patients.

Maggie looked up and smiled.

'She's fine—lovely, healthy baby. Was there a
problem?'

Ross laughed without humour. 'Oh, no, no problem.
It was like shelling peas!'

It was long after five before Lizzi was tidied up and
they got away from the hospital. Anne had rung Jenny
and asked her to hang on to Beth until they got there,
and she was giving her supper.

By the time they pulled up in Bloomingdale Way
outside Jake's house, Anne had already decided it was
too late and she was too tired to go shopping, so she

was surprised when Jake told her to go and change into something casual and he'd pick her up in ten minutes.

She collected Beth, avoided Jenny's questions yet again—some time, she knew, she was going to have to deal with them, but not tonight!—and quickly pulled on an old tracksuit.

Beth changed into her dungarees and a sweatshirt, and Anne noted absently that she had grown again and the legs were getting short.

Too bad, she thought, and hurried them out of the house just as Jake closed his front door behind him.

'All set?'

She nodded. 'More or less.'

'Why are we going in Jake's car?' Beth asked.

'Because mine won't go, for some reason,' Anne said through gritted teeth.

'That's OK,' Beth said cheerfully. 'I like Jake's car better, it's red. Can I go in the front?'

'No.'

'Why not?'

'Because your mother's going in the front next to me. Hop in.'

He held the door for Beth, and then fastened her seatbelt before sliding behind the wheel just as Anne settled herself in the front seat.

'Where would you like to go?'

'Sainsbury's is nearest,' she said promptly, and gave him directions. Within minutes they were wheeling a trolley round and Jake was filling it with fresh fruit and vegetables and unusual cheeses and meat, while Anne carefully selected her few items—eggs, spaghetti, tinned tomatoes, Cheddar cheese—and piled them neatly in the bottle section at the end of the trolley.

'Mum, can I have some new felt tips?' Beth asked as they passed the stationery counter.

'No——'

'Which ones?' Jake asked, and put the proffered packet in the trolley.

'Jake,' Anne began, but he smiled, his eyes glinting a warning.

'My treat,' he said firmly, and she subsided with a sigh. It wasn't much to be the first present to his daughter, and the least she could do was be gracious.

'Say thank you, Beth,' she prompted.

Jake smiled again. 'She already has—while you were struggling with your conscience!'

She sighed and picked up a packet of cheap envelopes.

'How big's your freezer?' he asked as he paused at the frozen meat section.

'Not awfully—why? Do you want to put something in it? It's empty at the moment—help yourself.'

'Great.' He picked up a bag of chicken pieces, a bag of diced pork, several lamb chops and some lean mince and threw them in the trolley, then moved on to the bread section.

Anne shook her head in disbelief. He was buying far more than her! What it must be to have money to burn.

With a sigh she picked up a couple of loaves of sliced white bread and put them in the trolley.

'You don't want to eat that junk,' he said firmly, and took them out of the trolley and replaced them with wholemeal and granary.

Anne opened her mouth to protest, and then shut it again. He was quite right, but she had got into the habit of buying cheaper cuts and economy loaves, and only just as much of anything as they needed, and there was Jake throwing half the shop into the trolley and not turning a hair!

'All done?' he asked, and she nodded.

'I'll just get a couple of bottles of wine and some beer, then, and we'll go.'

He wheeled the trolley to the nearest checkout, and when it was their turn he began unloading their things together.

'Jake, you're mixing everything up,' she told him, and he shrugged.

'That's OK, it's all yours anyway.'

'Mine? Don't be ridiculous!' She could feel the panic begin to rise, and took a deep breath to quell it. 'Look, Jake,' she said quietly, 'I know you only meant to help, but there's no way I can afford to pay for all those things—look at that trolley!'

'Don't worry, I'm paying,' he said calmly, and carried on unloading.

'No, you aren't! I won't let you—stop it!' she cried, but he carried on regardless.

'Jake, I mean it! Stop it now!'

'No. You need to eat, and so does Beth, and that's my responsibility——'

'No, it isn't, it's mine!'

He paused for a second. 'Do you really want to have a row about paternity rights and maintenance payments here at the checkout in front of all these people?' he asked her quietly, and then, turning away, he reached into the trolley again.

She grabbed his hands to stop him, and was startled by the sudden shock of electricity that ran between them.

Stunned, she met his eyes and saw an answering flare of desire in them before he tamped it down.

'Let me go, Annie,' he said quietly.

'Jake, please,' she begged, but he gently prised her fingers off his wrists and turned back to the trolley, putting the last few items on the checkout.

'Can I have some sweets?' Beth asked, looking at Jake.

'No——'

'Not tonight——'

They answered together, and Anne snorted. 'Don't tell me we agree on something, Hunter?' she said bitterly.

He stacked the last of the bags back into the trolley, handed over a wadge of notes and pocketed his change.

Anne noted the amount on the illuminated display, and as soon as they were seated in the car she got out her cheque-book and started to write him a cheque.

'Don't bother, I'll just tear it up.'

'I'll write out another, then,' she said defiantly.

'You'll run out of cheques before I give up, and anyway if what you say is true it'll only bounce,' he told her, and she shoved her cheque-book back into her handbag with an angry sigh.

'Damn you, you are interfering in my life and I won't have it!'

'Mummy, why are you fighting?' Beth asked curiously.

'Because I just bought her a present and she hasn't yet learnt to say thank you nicely, Beth,' he told her with a wicked twinkle.

She took a deep breath, met his warning glance and subsided into her seat, mumbling.

'Putting a hex on me, sweetheart?' he said in an undertone.

'Not before time,' she snapped. 'You wait, Hunter. This conversation is by no means over. There's a lot I have to say to you, starting with the shopping, via the felt pens, to the car. We need some ground rules.'

He nodded. 'I agree—and the first is adequate nutrition.'

'Our nutrition is perfectly adequate!'

'Bull. Why do you think you passed out on Sunday? Not even my ego believes it really had anything to do with seeing me again—although God knows if you have a conscience that should have been playing up enough to make you faint!'

He swung the car on to his drive and cut the engine, then turned round to Beth.

'Right, young lady, it's getting late. Do you suppose you could get ready for bed while your mummy and I bring in the shopping and put it away?'

Dear God, he's even taking over my role! Anne thought furiously, and stomped out of the car and into the house.

He followed her, his hands full, and suggested she put everything away while he brought it in.

By the time he brought the last bag in and shut the door, the house was freezing.

'We need to talk,' she said firmly.

'Let's put this lot away first.'

'Jake——'

'Later. Put the kettle on——'

'No. Listen to me, damn it! This is my house——'

'Shut up, Annie,' he said mildly. 'The frozen food is thawing while you rant and rave.'

He opened the little freezer section of her fridge and started packing it with all the things she couldn't afford.

Furiously angry, she whirled round and started finding a home for the other food. If he wanted to play her fairy godmother, she thought as she banged cupboard doors viciously, who was she to stop him?

As she turned she bumped into him, and, almost out of control, she stabbed her finger into his hard chest and glared at him. 'OK—this time, I'll let you get away with it, but don't you ever pull a stunt like that again, do you hear? I won't be humiliated in public——'

'I didn't humiliate you! I just bought the shopping——'

'But I couldn't afford it, and then we had to have a row about it right there in front of everybody——'

'We didn't have to, Annie. You started it. You could just have given in gracefully, but you had to get up on your high horse——'

'*My* high horse?' She shoved past him and seized a packet of pasta. 'Who was it throwing ten-pound notes around like confetti?'

'Oh, for God's sake, shut up! Have you any idea what the courts would have ordered me to pay you in maintenance for our daughter over the past seven years? Have you? Do you have any idea how much money I actually owe you?'

She turned away and threw the pasta into a cupboard. 'Keep you voice down, please—and you owe me nothing for the support of my daughter.'

'Our daughter.'

She turned back to face him. 'You can't buy your way into our family, Jake.'

Their eyes locked in battle, hers angry, his grimly determined.

'What do I have to do to win your affection, Annie? How can I prove my intentions are sincere?'

She stared him down. 'You can't. You blew it, years ago. You're a playboy, Jake. I can't stop you from seeing Beth, and I wouldn't want to, but I won't have you flashing your money around and spoiling her rotten, undermining my authority and making her feel I've cheated her when I'm busting a gut to keep us afloat!'

'But that's my point, Annie. You don't have to any more. I want to help. Please let me.'

She turned away, refusing to be moved by his reasonable tone. 'I don't want your help. Just don't hinder me, either. I want that part back in my car so I can use it tomorrow, and I want you out of my house now. It's bad enough having to work with you without you clogging up my home life as well.'

'You're shutting me out, Annie, but it won't work.'

'Try me!' she challenged, and then caught the look in his eye. She got the distinct, uneasy feeling she'd just thrown down the gauntlet, and he'd picked it up—smiling.

CHAPTER FOUR

JAKE'S car was gone in the morning, and hers, Annie was pleased to note, was working again—as well as it ever had.

At least the snow had thawed during the night and the road surface was safer to drive on, because if she was honest the brakes were a bit suspect.

She chewed her lip and wondered if perhaps Jake had been right about the safety of the car. The garage had seemed quite respectable, but she knew enough to know that she knew nothing, and she would have been easy to hoodwink.

She crashed the gears and turned into the hospital car park, only a few minutes late, and ran up to the ward.

Sister greeted her with a smile.

'Hello, Anne.'

'Hi. How's everything?'

'OK. Lizzi Hamilton would like a word, if you've got time.'

She popped her head round the door and found Lizzi propped up on her pillows, her little daughter suckling hungrily at her breast.

'She certainly doesn't seem to have suffered too badly, does she?' Anne said with a smile.

Lizzi laughed softly. 'Isn't she just amazing? I can't believe it was so easy. Ross tells me I made a tremendous fuss, but I really can't remember!'

Anne was stunned. Perhaps Jake was right—again.

She almost groaned. It was getting to be a habit. Couldn't he be wrong about something?

'How are you feeling today? Bruised, I should think.'

Lizzi nodded. 'Oh, yes, very sore, but I gather I didn't need many stitches. It was my bones that were the problem, and by the time her head was moulded it was really quite small! I expect the poor little mite had a mother and father of a headache.'

'I often wonder what it feels like,' Anne said, perching on the bed to get a closer look at the little girl. 'She's really very lovely.'

The door opened and shut behind her, and she knew before she turned round that it was Jake.

'How's my favourite patient this morning?' he said with a broad grin, and, stationing himself right by the bed so his legs pressed against Anne's thigh, he leant over and brushed the baby's cheek with his long, blunt finger. 'She looks none the worse for her ordeal, anyway.'

'Oh, she's fine,' Lizzi said indulgently.

'And how are you?'

'Very well. I have to thank you—I gather from Ross that without you she probably wouldn't have made it.'

He flushed slightly and gave a small grunt of embarrassed laughter. 'I'm sorry I had to bully you so much, but I knew you could do it, and when her heartbeat dropped——' He shrugged eloquently and touched the baby's cheek again. 'What are you going to call her?'

'Sarah, I think. We haven't quite decided.'

'I like it. Good, strong biblical name.'

'Like Jacob,' Anne said drily.

'And Elizabeth.'

'Of course, you've got a daughter called Beth, haven't you?' Lizzi said.

'Yes,' they said in unison, and Lizzi looked from one to the other, her expression slightly puzzled.

'Yes, I have,' Anne added, her eyes daring Jake to intervene. 'She's nearly seven.'

Lizzi nodded. 'Jo said she was gorgeous.'

'She is,' Jake agreed. 'Quite delightful. Lizzi, we're going to have to be getting on, I'm afraid, we have a clinic. I'm glad things are OK.'

'Me, too. And thanks again.'

He grinned. 'You're welcome. Come on, Annie. Time to do some work.'

He moved away from the bed at last, and she stood up somewhat shakily. The contact of his legs against hers had practically burnt a hole in them, or so it seemed.

Damn him, why was she so aware of him—and why, suddenly, was he so hell bent on teasing her with her awareness? He never used to. Perhaps he hadn't realised, but now! Now he was pressing his advantage ruthlessly, and he knew it.

As they walked out of the room, he grinned at her wickedly.

'Morning, gorgeous,' he said under his breath. 'How's my favourite daughter's mother this morning?'

She glared at him. 'I don't think it's a good idea to talk about it at work—you know what hotbeds of gossip hospitals are.'

He sobered. 'You're probably right. We don't want anyone to know until Beth does—by the way, does Jo know?'

'That she's yours?' Anne shook her head. 'My parents do, and Duncan, but no one else.'

The lift doors were open when they arrived, and Jake pressed the button for the ground floor and then lounged against the wall with his hands in his pockets, his suit jacket falling open to show the slight strain of his shirt over the taut planes of his chest and the way his hands had stretched his trousers so that they tugged across his hips. It was a lazy, consciously sexual pose, and she felt heat brush her cheeks.

She looked up and met his laughing eyes.

'You can have me, Annie, any time you like. You only have to say the word.'

She turned away. 'You're despicable. Stop flaunting yourself at me, Jake.'

'Me?' He laughed. 'You're just aware of me, Annie. I'm not doing anything.'

'You're being deliberately provocative, and you know it.'

She didn't hear him move, but the subtly intoxicating fragrance of his aftershave teased her senses, and her skin shivered.

'Am I provoking you, Annie? I hope so,' he murmured, his warm breath brushing the nape of her neck below her hair.

'Yes, you're provoking me to anger,' she said crossly, and turned round to find him barely inches away, his dark brown eyes alive with laughter—and something else, something much, much more dangerous.

'Jake, please,' she begged breathlessly.

His hand came up and tucked a strand of hair behind her ear. 'My pleasure,' he said softly, and then the lift bumped to a halt and the doors slid open.

With a sigh of regret, he turned towards the doors and smiled at the nurses waiting to come in.

'Morning, ladies,' he said cheerfully.

They all chorused, 'Good morning!', their adoring eyes following him as he walked away from the lift.

Anne trailed after him slowly.

How could she possibly manage to work with him

for the next week and a half until Jo and Alex got back?

She sighed heavily, remembering his promise about Beth. Never mind the next week and a half—what about the next decade?

Damn you, Jo Harding, she thought crossly. How could you do this to me?

The antenatal clinic went slowly. Every problem there could be, there was, and none of it was exactly enhanced by her total inability to concentrate on anything but the look in Jake's eyes when he had nearly kissed her in the lift.

The first major glitch was a woman who was rather breathless and complaining of indigestion, although she was only thirty-three weeks pregnant. She seemed to Anne to be rather larger than she should have been, and she also complained that the baby seemed to be much more active than before.

'I'll just get the registrar to have a look at you,' Anne told her, and slipped out of the cubicle. Jake was in his office writing up notes, and she went in and closed the door.

'Problems, Annie?' he asked, still writing, his dark head bent over the desk. His hair looked thick and soft and glossy, and she had an overwhelming urge to touch it. . .

'Mmm. Mrs Partington—she's got polyhydramnios—at least, I think it is. She's huge for her dates, says she's got much bigger just recently, and I'm having difficulty feeling the baby. There's also what could be a fluid thrill, but I'm not sure if it's abnormal.'

He put down the pen and leant back, steepling his fingers against his lips.

'Hmm. Any previous children?'

'It's her second. I though she was having twins at

first, but I can hardly feel anything, and with twins there are masses of bumps.'

He nodded. 'OK, I'll have a look and we'll get a scan done. Either it's a multiple pregnancy, or she does have an excess of fluid as you suspect, which means the baby's anencephalic, got oesophageal or duodenal atresia, or she's haemorrhaging. Whatever, we need to deal with it. Hopefully you're being too cautious.'

After he examined her, though, he was forced to agree.

'It's polyhydramnios all right,' he said while they were waiting for the scan. 'We just have to find out why.'

'Will you admit her?'

He shrugged. 'Depends. If she's very uncomfortable, we can have her in and take some of the fluid off whenever necessary, but when she goes into labour she might need a section to prevent prolapse of the cord when her membranes rupture. If there's the slightest likelihood of her going into labour, I want her here.'

He handed her the notes. 'Let's wait and see. I have to get on, there's someone else waiting to see me. Call me when she goes in for her scan.'

The scan at least showed quite clearly that the baby was healthy and not deformed in any way, and there was certainly only the one. However, they were unable to make out the usually visible fluid-filled stomach and bladder that in a normal baby showed as dark areas in the abdominal cavity.

'Looks like oesophageal atresia,' Jake said, and explained to the worried patient that her baby had probably developed with a condition where the oesophagus, instead of connecting to the stomach, ended in a blind pouch, and because the baby was unable to swallow, the fluid was building up around it.

'Nobody really understands the mechanics of fluid balance in the uterus,' he continued, 'but we know what happens when it goes wrong, and we usually know what it indicates. We can keep the fluid level down to a certain extent, but your labour will have to be monitored very carefully, or you may even need a Caesarean section. Then immediately your baby's born it will be taken to Great Ormond Street in London for surgery, because the condition has to be corrected immediately, after which he or she will recover very quickly.'

He smiled reassuringly. 'It's really quite common, and you shouldn't worry about it, but we have to take very good care of you from now on. What about your domestic arrangements?'

'Oh, my husband's just been made redundant, so I suppose he could look after the little one—how long do you think you're talking about?'

Jake pursed his lips thoughtfully. 'Two—maybe three weeks? I'd like to keep you going as long as possible, so the baby's as old as we can reasonably achieve, but that all depends on how big you get and how much fluid we are able to remove. Sometimes it's replaced almost instantly, and then we have no choice but to induce you or do a section fairly quickly, for your own comfort.'

He smiled. 'There's a definite limit to how miserable we'll let you get before we interfere, don't worry. If it all gets too much, we'll sort you out. Is your husband here now?'

She nodded unhappily.

'Perhaps you'd like me to have a word with him, then he can leave you here and go home for your things. Would that help?'

'Oh, dear—there's so much to do at home. . .'

Jake laid his hand on her shoulder. 'Is it more important than your baby?'

'No—oh, no. . .'

'OK. Get dressed and go and find your husband, and we'll have a chat in my office before we admit you.'

They found a nurse to help Mrs Partington struggle into her clothes, and then Anne went on to examine some of the other waiting patients.

By the time everyone was all sorted out and they were able to go for lunch, it was one-thirty and Jake was due in Theatre at two.

'Will you be at home this evening?' he asked throu' a mouthful of salad.

'Probably—why?'

'Thought I'd pop in and see Beth, but I don't suppose I'll be finished all that early. What time does she go to bed?'

'Seven.'

'Hmm.' He gulped down his coffee and stood up. 'I'll try and make it—don't say anything in case I'm late.'

She was just finishing her coffee when Maggie rushed in, grabbed a Danish pastry and a coffee and came to join her.

'Hi!'

'Maggie! How are you? Tell me all about it. I still can't believe you and Ben are getting married in ten days.'

'Nor can I!' Maggie bit a chunk off her Danish, swiped her tongue round her gooey lips and grinned. 'Life's just fantastic at the moment—even my grandmother's behaving herself. She's so self-satisfied because she got us together that she's even deferring to our wishes over the wedding plans—which reminds me, are you off?'

Anne nodded. 'Should be. I think the other firm's on take over the weekend, so we have a bit of peace—and Beth's away, as well, staying with my parents for the week from Sunday night onwards. I expect Jake will be on call, so yes, I can definitely come, barring World War Three or whatever!'

'Great! Do you know when Jo and Alex are back from their holiday?'

Anne shook her head doubtfully. 'Next Friday, isn't it? I'm honestly not sure. No doubt she'll be in touch.'

'Just so long as they are; I'd hate them to miss it, but I've got no intention of putting it off—I want Ben tied to me legally before anything else can go wrong!'

Anne gave a faint smile. How wonderful it must be to be making wedding plans. First Jo, now Maggie. She doubted if she would ever get married now. After all, who would want a woman of thirty-three with a seven-year-old daughter?

Jake, a voice nagged at her, but she dismissed it. Jake wasn't a contender that any right-minded woman would take seriously, not with his track record.

She sighed.

'You sound tired—lots of talk about old times with Jake keeping you up at night?' Maggie asked with studied innocence.

'Are you kidding?' She sighed again. 'Jake and I have nothing to talk about.'

'Not even Beth?'

Anne's head snapped up, and she met Maggie's guileless blue eyes with horror. 'Why should we talk about Beth?' she asked as casually as she could manage.

Maggie looked away quickly. 'Forgive me—it's none of my business.'

Anne's shoulders drooped. 'Jo must have said something—I didn't think she knew.'

'Jo? Oh, no, Jo didn't say a word, Annie. I just guessed—they're so alike. You forget, I don't know them as well as Jo, so I probably see them more clearly.'

Anne worried her bottom lip with her teeth. 'He wants to marry me.'

'That's great—so go for it!' Maggie said, her voice full of youthful enthusiasm.

'I wish I dared, but—Maggie, if you'd known him. . . He was such a playboy, just a natural flirt, out with a different girl every night—I wouldn't dare trust him.'

Maggie wiped her hands on her napkin and looked Anne in the eye. 'That was then. This is now. How do you know he hasn't changed?'

'I don't—but I don't know that he has, either. How could I expose Beth to his fickle affections? If she found her father after all these years, just to lose him again—that's too much to expect her to cope with.'

'And you, I suspect,' Maggie said quietly. 'You still love him, don't you?'

'No!' she denied, a little too quickly. 'He drives me insane. . .he's so high-handed, and he's forever dropping in—did you know he's living in the other half of my house for now?'

Maggie shook her head. 'No, I didn't. That must be very awkward.'

'Awkward? It's downright impossible!' She stood up and flicked the crumbs from her skirt. 'Sorry, I have to run—new admissions to clerk. I'll see you around.'

'Annie?'

She turned back. 'Yes?'

'I'm here if you need me.'

She smiled slowly. 'Thanks—thanks, Maggie. I'm glad things are working out for you.'

She left then, and made her way back to the maternity unit, deep in thought.

She spent the first two hours on the gynae ward, clerking the new admissions, then made her way up to Obstetrics.

As she walked into the ward, she saw the door of Lizzi Hamilton's room open and great gales of laughter coming from inside. There was a sudden pop like a muffled gunshot, and a cheer went up.

Ross popped his head out. 'Anne! Come and join us.'

She veered right and went into the crowded little room.

'Two visitors at a time, I see,' she said with a wink at the laughing woman in the bed.

'Annie! Have a glass of champagne.'

She looked round and smiled. 'Is there a surgeon out there in the hospital at all this afternoon?' she asked mildly.

Ross was there, of course, and Oliver Henderson, the other consultant general surgeon with his very pregnant wife Bron and their little daughter, and Michael and Clare Barrington, and Jake in theatre greens with a cap stuck on his head at a crazy angle and a paper cup in his hand.

Even Sister had unbent enough to join them, and passed Anne a paper cup with a dribble of champagne in the bottom.

In the middle of it all young Sarah Hamilton lay fast asleep, oblivious.

Jake drained his cup and dropped a kiss on Lizzi's cheek. 'I have to go back to Theatre—I hope I get the right instruments put in my hand. Fine stuff, this!'

They all laughed—all except Anne, whose face creased in a worried frown.

'Don't worry, Annikins, I'm quite sober,' he said under his breath as he passed her, winking wickedly.

Somehow she doubted it, but she didn't feel she could make a fuss in front of all the other surgeons present who were probably about to do just the same thing!

Draining her cup, she gave Lizzi a rather tight smile and excused herself to carry on with her duties.

The rest of the afternoon passed routinely enough, and she was able to get away on time for once.

Even so, by the time she was back and had fed Beth and sorted out her homework, chivvied her into the bath and they were settled down in the sitting-room in front of the gas fire with a book, it was after half-past six.

Good job I didn't mention that Jake was hoping to visit, she thought, and was shocked at the little pang that she recognised as disappointment.

She was even more shocked at the sudden race of her heart when the doorbell rang mere seconds later.

Beth, of course, was there first, throwing open the door and welcoming Jake with her gappy smile and uptilted face beaming her pleasure at his arrival.

'Come in,' she instructed, but he shook his head.

'In a minute. There's something I want your mother to look at first.' He beckoned her down the hall, and, puzzled, she went to the doorway and peered out into the dimly lit street.

Parked by the kerb was a shiny red Volvo—not one of the big estates, but a smaller hatchback, the sort Anne might have aspired to in about three years' time, if that.

Jake was dangling the keys under her nose.

'*Voilà*! Your car, Dr Gabriel!' he said with a confident grin, like a magician pulling a rabbit from a hat.

Beth turned her head and looked up at Anne. 'Mummy! You didn't say we were getting another new car! Wow—and it's red, too!'

Anne ignored her daughter, and glared across her head at Jake. 'No,' she said clearly. 'Watch my lips, Jacob. N-O. Come in, Beth.'

She gripped her daughter firmly by the arm and towed her back in over the step, closing the door on Jake's face.

Or at least she tried to close the door. His foot, however, got in the way and interfered somewhat with her intentions.

Giving up, she released her hold on the door and walked instead into the sitting-room, picking up the telephone.

'What are you doing?'

'Calling the police.'

His hand came round and he depressed the button, cutting her off. 'What are you going to report—the opposite of a stolen vehicle?'

'You're trespassing,' she gritted.

'There's no such thing as trespass,' he told her calmly.

'Why are you calling the police?' Beth asked, puzzled.

'Because she doesn't know how to accept presents yet, Beth. Perhaps she just hasn't had very much practice.'

Beth sucked her bottom lip. 'She always makes me say thank you,' she said doubtfully.

Anne swivelled round and met her daughter's troubled gaze. 'I have also taught you to say no,' she said through clenched teeth.

'Only to strangers—and Jake's not a stranger, are you, Jake?'

'No—just an interfering busybody,' Anne muttered.

Jake smiled infuriatingly. 'I'm neither—I'm just a very old friend.'

'How long have you known Mummy?' Beth asked him.

'Nearly twelve years,' he replied, his eyes never leaving Anne's face.

'Why haven't I ever seen you before, then?' she asked now, puzzled.

'Jake's been away,' Anne said. 'Now run along——'

'Where?'

'In America, mostly,' Jake told her quietly.

Beth looked up at him. 'My daddy's in America,' she said innocently.

Jake opened his mouth, caught Anne's horrified expression and shut it.

'Darling, run and clean your teeth and come back down for a story—I just want to have a word with my *old friend*.' She emphasised the last two words heavily, and Jake's eyebrows twitched.

As Beth left the room, Anne closed the door firmly behind her and turned to face Jake, her anger barely held in check.

'Don't you dare tell her!'

'Why? Don't you think she has a right to know either?'

She sagged back against the wall. 'Of course she has a right to know, but not now—not like this, when we're angry——'

'I'm not angry.'

'No—just bloody awkward! I thought I'd made it absolutely clear that I wouldn't accept charity from you——'

'The car is not for you,' he said clearly, emphasising every word distinctly. 'It is for Beth—to ensure that she is safe, and that you are safe, as long as she needs you.'

'There's nothing wrong with my car——'

'Oh, come on, Annie, it's a wreck! You know it's not safe.'

'Then I'll sell it and we'll go everywhere on the bus, but I won't be beholden to you——'

He sighed and dropped on to the sofa, sprawled comfortably, head tipped back to look up at her.

'She's my daughter, Annie,' he said quietly. 'I have a right to protect her and to provide for her—a right that the courts would be only too happy to point out to you, I'm sure.'

She lowered herself miserably to the chair. 'Jake, I can't allow you to do this—surely you can see that? Everybody will talk.'

'Tell them your father bought it for you.'

She rolled her eyes. 'Have you any idea just how far a seven-year-old can spread information, and how fast? No one would believe me.'

Jake rose easily to his feet and came over to her, squatting in front of her and taking her hands in his. They were big and warm and hard, engulfing her smaller ones and spreading fire through her body. His thumbs moved lazily against her pulse-points, fanning the flames.

'Annie, they're all going to know, sooner or later. Beth and I are too alike—damn it, even I can see it. It's like looking in a mirror. How long do you really think it's going to be before everyone starts talking?'

She dragged her hands back and tucked them into her lap. 'I'll pay you back—you can consider it a loan. How much was it?'

He snorted and rose to his feet. 'About three years' maintenance. I still owe you four, but just at the moment I can't afford it.'

'Just how much, Jake?'

'Forget it, Annie. Just take the damn thing—on loan, if you must, but please, for Beth?'

Anne chewed her lip worriedly. 'Do you really think my car is so bad?'

He turned back to her, crouching down again and unfolding her hands from her lap, wrapping them in one of his and lifting them to his lips.

'Yes—yes, I do, and you're both much too precious to me to risk losing when there's something so simple I can do about it.'

Anne felt her breath catch in her throat. How desperately she wanted to belong to him, to know that she was precious, cherished. . .

She looked up and met his eyes, and felt a swift shaft of desire rip through her. Her teeth worried her lip again, and he lifted his hand, his thumb dragging softly over the fullness of her lip.

'Don't,' he whispered, 'you'll hurt yourself.'

Their eyes met and locked, and deep inside Anne felt some invisible barrier give way, making room for him again in her heart.

As if he sensed it, his hand moved round and cupped the back of her head, urging her forwards gently until their lips brushed.

With a ragged groan deep in his throat he curled his other hand into her hair and took her mouth with a hunger that both shocked and thrilled her.

Finally he lifted his head, his breath coming hard and fast, his eyes glittering with passion.

'Does that mean we're keeping it?'

Their heads whipped round. Beth, wide-eyed and

fascinated, was standing in the doorway in her pyjamas, a teddy in one hand and a book in the other. Judging by the expression on her face, she had been there altogether longer than either of the adults would have wished.

'I think so—you'll have to ask your mother,' Jake said, his voice gravelly and slightly uneven.

He stood up awkwardly and went and sat on the sofa, hooking an ankle up on to the other knee. His breathing was still slightly ragged, and Anne had to fight to keep her lips from smiling.

'Yes, darling, we're keeping it for now. Jake's going to lend it to us.'

'Yippee!' Beth shrieked, and threw herself at him, wrapping her little arms round his waist and squeezing tight.

'Steady,' he laughed, 'you'll crush me! Here, how about reading some of this book?'

He picked a book out of the bookcase by the end of the sofa, and Beth snuggled up next to him in the circle of his arm, her head against his chest, the teddy on his lap looking at the book too.

Anne rested her head against the back of the chair and let their voices wash over her. If she didn't allow her thoughts to stray, so that her memory couldn't conjure up the spectre of all his other women, it would be so easy to pretend that they were a real family, a real mother and father going through the usual established bedtime routine.

And then later, when the children—one or maybe two more—were tucked up in bed, they would sit together and watch television or read, or just hold hands and stare into the flames, and then when the cat had been let out and the milk bottles put on the step and the sitting-room tidied, he would take her hand

and lead her up the stairs, and there, quietly so as not to disturb the children, they would reaffirm their love with soft sighs and tender caresses, building gradually to urgent whispers and fevered seeking, until with muffled cries their joy would overspill and wrap them round with love.

Then they would sleep, tangled together on the crumpled sheets, their hearts beating as one. . .

CHAPTER FIVE

FINALS night was always a party night, and that finals night party in Bristol was a party to end all parties.

There was such a mixed bag of emotion—joy, regret, anticipation and apprehension about the years ahead, everyone full of plans and hopes and dreams, and yet, as always at the end of a chapter, a sense of loss, an awareness that old friendships would wane and new ones would take their place.

For Jo Harding, Jake Hunter and Anne Gabriel, the parting would be a savage wrench. Jo and Jake were off to London, not the same hospital but close enough to see each other fairly regularly. Anne was heading to Birmingham, further afield but still easily accessible.

There were endless promises to keep in touch, and jokes about whose would be the first wedding, although they all expected it to be Anne's, as she and Duncan were engaged.

Except that they weren't, although only Anne knew that. Oh, she had a ring, but she had bought it for herself after she and Duncan had finally called a halt to a relationship that was evidently going nowhere. They blamed it on the distance between Bristol and Edinburgh, but the truth was that since Jake had ambled into her life with his reckless grin and blatant sensuality her love for Duncan had faded. True, the distance between them hadn't helped, but every time her childhood sweetheart took her in his arms she found herself wishing they were Jake's arms, Jake's lips—and she couldn't live a lie.

At least, not that one. There was another, possibly bigger lie, that she lived now day by day, given credibility by Duncan's periodic phone calls to try and talk her back to him.

She had told everyone that they were engaged, because that way she could fend off other erstwhile suitors and at the same time continue to spend time with Jake without arousing his suspicions.

Not that there was much time to spend with him. If she wasn't cramming for her exams, which she was most of the time, then Jake was out or in the pub or at a nightclub or at a party with yet another nurse or pretty young medical student or physio.

They fell for him like ninepins, and sometimes he would ask Anne to go with him to a party to give him some protection from one or other of his current women who had become overdemanding.

His success with women was legendary, and his reputation was by no means unfounded.

Anne knew that for a fact. She had taken one look at him and her heart had nose-dived off the edge of a cliff.

Nearly four years later she was still falling, but it was a fall that would end with her heart dashed on the rocks, she knew. As far as Jake was concerned, she didn't even exist as a woman—and that was no surprise. She was just a little brown mouse after all, and Jake was one of the beautiful people.

Her eyes found him automatically in the seething, laughing throng, dancing with a bevvy of women, as if one at a time wasn't enough. She didn't want to watch him, but somehow her eyes strayed back time and time again. Sometimes he would see her and wave, but, whatever, he seemed to be avoiding her.

The party was in full swing when he left, a pretty girl

on his arm as usual. Making some incoherent excuse to her dancing partner, Anne slipped out of the fire exit and stood in the semi-darkness of the hot June night, trying not to think about where Jake was headed and why. She swallowed the lump in her throat and tried to ignore the pain. She wouldn't think about them together, about his strong, supple body entwined with that girl's, about fevered caresses and murmured endearments, the feel of his skin like hot satin beneath her palms——

'Are you OK?'

Anne looked up, started, to see Jo Harding's wide blue-green eyes gazing worriedly at her.

'Just a bit tired. I think I'll go on back now, actually. I've got a headache.'

'Poor love—take some aspirin. You can't party-poop, it's finals night!'

Anne made a feeble attempt at a smile. 'Sorry, Jo, I have to. I take it you're staying?'

Jo laughed, shaking back her mane of red hair exultantly. 'Are you kidding? I'm not going to bed tonight at all—and neither should you!'

She whirled away through the doors, still laughing, in the arms of another old friend.

Had Anne but known it, that was a sage piece of advice. She should have listened, should have stayed at the party and ignored her feelings for Jake, but she didn't, she made her way back to the tall Victorian house in Clifton that she shared with Jake and Jo and three other medical students, and climbed the stairs towards the attic room that had been her home for the past almost-four years.

Her foot on the bottom of the attic stairs, she hesitated for a moment by the open door of Jake's room.

In the spill of light from the landing, she saw that instead of the usual chaotic jumble of clothes and textbooks, there was a neat stack of boxes crammed with his possessions—his stereo system, books, clothes and so forth. There was a Mickey Mouse tie that she had given him hanging out of the side of a suitcase, and Alfred, Jake's skeleton, slouched drunkenly in the corner, waiting for the next adventure.

Jake's bed was unmade, the sheets rumpled, and Anne went in and sat on the bed and wondered how she would get through her life without him.

He had been such a wonderful friend, cheerful and supportive, always there to jolly her along. The only time he'd been distant was when she'd become 'engaged' to Duncan, and she had assumed then that he felt his support was no longer necessary.

Little did he know.

She picked up his pillow and smoothed the cover, holding it to her face and breathing deeply to inhale his scent. It was so dear, so familiar, and she would miss him so much. . .

A choked sob rose in her throat, and she buried her face in the pillow and let the tears fall.

The bed dipped beside her, and a comforting arm wrapped around her back and folded her hard against a solid chest.

'Annie?'

She lifted her head, ignoring the tears that had tracked down her face, and, lifting her hand, she laid her fingers wonderingly against his stubble-rough jaw.

'What are you doing here? I thought. . .'

'What did you think?'

She sniffed and wiped her cheeks on the backs of her hands. 'You left the party. . .'

'With Judy. I took her home, that's all. She was a

little the worse for wear. When I got back, you'd left. Jo said you'd be here.'

His thumb brushed lightly against her damp cheek, dragging the skin gently.

'Why the tears, Annie?'

'Oh, it's silly. It's just—I'm going to miss you, Jake. I've got so used to having you around——'

A fresh tear welled and slipped down her cheek, and he tracked it with his finger, scooping it up and touching it to his tongue.

'Don't cry,' he murmured, and then she was in his arms and he was kissing the tears away, his lips gentle and undemanding.

'I'm going to miss you, too, Annie,' he whispered against her hair, and then he released her, standing up and fiddling with the contents of one of the boxes while she blew her nose and pulled herself together.

She put down his pillow and stood up on uncooperative legs.

'Do you want a coffee?' she asked unsteadily.

'Not really.' He turned to face her. 'Do you know what I really want?'

She shook her head slowly, unsure of the sudden intensity of his gaze.

'I want you,' he said, with quiet conviction. 'Stay with me, Annie. Give me tonight.'

Her heart stopped and then started again, crashing against her ribs. Had she dreamt it? Her eyes scanned his face, desperately searching for the truth. Was it just pity for a little brown mouse all alone on finals night? Or was it just that he was a highly sensual and erotic man and she was a woman, alone with him and just tipsy enough to let down her guard?

Or perhaps it was just his way of saying goodbye.

Whatever, Annie needed him as she had never

needed him before. It was crazy, probably the most stupid thing she had ever done, but she was going to do it anyway, and hang the consequences—if she could only make her feet move.

'Annie?' he said softly, his voice raw with need, and suddenly her feet were working again, carrying her towards him. He opened his arms and she walked into them, heedless of the clamour of her common sense.

His mouth closed over hers, hard and hot and hungry, and his tongue teased her lips until they parted for him on a sigh of surrender.

Her dress fell away with a whisper of sound, leaving her naked except for a tiny scrap of lace that did little to hide her mysteries from him.

Holding her at arm's length, he let his eyes trace over each soft curve, and she felt his glittering gaze like a caress in the heat of the night.

Finally his eyes returned to hers and they burned with a promise that took away the last fragments of her breath.

Slowly, unhurriedly, he stripped off his clothes, giving her time to study him as he had studied her.

And, dear God, he was beautiful! Strong and straight, his skin still tanned from last year, deeply shadowed by the crisp curls that sprang from his chest and arrowed down over the flat, taut plane of his abdomen to flare again around the heavy fullness of his masculinity.

Unable to breathe, hardly able to stand, she reached out to him in the half-light from the landing, clinging to his fingers as they meshed with hers, as he drew her closer and folded her hard against his chest.

There were no words. There was nothing to say, only soft sighs and tender caresses as they lay together in the tangle of his sheets and brought each other to the brink of fulfilment.

Then she felt his weight on her, felt her body yield to his possession, and in that possession felt the gift of his vulnerability.

Beneath her palms his body trembled, his skin sweat-slicked and supple, and as their passion spiralled into ecstasy she heard him cry her name, like a prayer in the darkness of the night.

He held her then, cradled against his chest, and when she tried to speak he silenced her with the pressure of his fingers against her lips, almost as if he was afraid to break the spell.

'Don't say anything,' he murmured, 'just let me hold you.'

So she rested her head on his chest and listened to the steady rhythm of his heart, and wondered if anyone had ever loved like this before.

He woke her later with the brush of his lips, and as she turned into his arms he loved her again, taking her to new heights and greater depths, and she gave him everything she had, all the warmth and strength and heart-shaking sincerity of her love until they fell again into the boiling maelstrom of passion they had evoked.

She woke again as the first rays of sun turned the sky to flame, to find Jake propped up on one elbow gazing down at her with his darkly hooded eyes, their expression curiously unreadable.

'Jake,' she began, but he silenced her again.

'Hush,' he said softly, 'one last time, Annie.'

It was a farewell to end all farewells, touched with a tender desperation that nearly broke her heart.

His touch was so careful, so infinitely gentle, as if he was afraid she would shatter, and when it was over and he lifted his head his lashes were spiked with tears.

Rolling to the side, he curled Anne against him and held her as she wept, and then finally she slept again, her sleep haunted with dreams in which she woke to find him gone.

When she did wake, it was to find him dressed and sitting on the edge of the bed. The boxes had gone, and Alfred too, his sightless vigil ended.

'You're going!' she exclaimed, struggling to sit up.

'In a minute. I need to pack the bedclothes into the car.'

Her mouth opened and closed again, no words offering themselves to the moment.

'I'll get dressed,' she managed eventually, and, climbing out of bed, she scooped up her dress and underwear and ran up the attic stairs to her room.

Blindly, her fingers shaking and uncooperative, she tugged on an old pair of jeans and a T-shirt, then ran back downstairs just as he came in again through the front door.

She went hesitantly down to meet him, her heart pounding, her knees shaking violently from the knowledge of his imminent departure. She must explain, now, before it was too late, about her non-existent engagement. There must be no secrets. She would somehow wriggle out of her contract in Birmingham and join him in London—somehow she'd get a job there so they could be together. God knew she couldn't bear to be apart from him——

'OK?' he asked quietly.

She nodded. 'Fine. Can I get you a coffee?'

'No, I must get on.'

She hesitated, unsure where to start, or how. 'Jake, about Duncan,' she began.

He shook his head. 'This needn't make any difference to either of us, Annie. You're going to marry

Duncan, and I'm going to finish sowing my wild oats and see the world—America, Africa—who knows? By the time I get back you'll have a whole clutch of kids and a mortgage and God knows what!'

He gave a slightly shaky laugh, and reached out his arms.

'Thank you, Annie—for everything.'

She went into his arms automatically, too shocked to protest at his words. What did he mean, it needn't make any difference? To him, perhaps not, but to her? She squeezed her eyes shut against the tears. What kind of a fool was she to expect declarations of undying love from him? Of course he was going—what else had she expected from the biggest playboy in the world?

Later she would be glad she hadn't finished telling him about Duncan, but then she was simply glad he was going so that she could fall apart in private.

Except that Jo ran in then, flung her arms around them both and hugged them hard.

'Thank God you're still here—I thought I'd miss you. When are you off?'

'Any minute,' he said gruffly, and Jo shot him a searching look.

'You OK?'

He nodded. 'I'll see you in a couple of months—you both know how to contact me, don't you? My parents will know where to find me, and I expect addresses and phone numbers as soon as you have them.'

Jo threw herself into his arms with a hiccuping sob, and he hugged her back, his eyes squeezed tight shut.

'Goodbye, you old reprobate,' she said, her voice clogged with tears, and then it was Annie's turn for one last wordless hug.

Jo watched him climb into his overloaded little car

and drive off, then turned back to see Anne staring sightlessly after him.

'It's not so far from Birmingham,' Jo teased gently, and then the dam burst, and Jo held out her arms and gathered Anne up against her breast and cradled her like a child while her heart broke and shattered into a million pieces.

'Why are you crying?'

Anne opened her eyes. Jake was crouched in front of her, his dark eyes concerned.

She dashed the tears away from her eyes and sniffed. 'I didn't know I was.'

His voice was gentle. 'What's wrong, my love?'

'Nothing—I was just remembering.'

'Us?'

She sniffed again. 'There was no "us", Jake—that's the trouble. We never had a relationship.'

He sighed and stood up, running his hands through his hair. 'We had a hell of a relationship, Annie—it just wasn't physical.' He turned towards her again, his eyes burning like live coals. 'But it could be.'

'No.'

He sighed again, then gave a rueful little laugh and threw his hands up in defeat. 'I give up—for now. Come and look at the car. I'll show you all the controls, and then you can take it out for a run while I sit with Beth.'

She blinked and looked round. 'Where is Beth?'

'In bed—I tucked her up and read her another story. Don't worry, she's fine. We thought you were asleep.'

She unfolded her legs from the chair and stood up, wincing. 'Tell me all about the car, then, if I have to have it.'

He laughed ruefully. 'Graciousness never was your strong point, was it, Annikins?'

'Don't call me that!' she snapped, secretly touched by his reversion to her pet name.

He chuckled and threw her the car keys. 'Come on.'

He showed her the controls, told her the car was three years old and had done twenty-five thousand miles, had a full service history and was still under the manufacturer's warranty, and then sent her off for a drive.

Anne was relieved that it wasn't brand-new as she had first suspected, but her conscience and pride still pricked her for accepting it. She told herself it was for Beth, and that Jake could easily afford it, but even so. . .

When she went back into the house after her drive, she found Jake in the kitchen, fossicking about in the freezer compartment of her fridge.

'I'm starving—mind if I find something to eat?'

She tossed the keys on to the table. 'Help yourself— you paid for it all.'

His eyebrows twitched, but he ignored the comment. 'How was the car?'

'Very nice.' She drew a deep breath. 'Thank you, Jake.'

He stopped what he was doing and turned towards her, searching her face. Then he smiled, a gentle, understanding smile because he knew what it had cost her to say the words.

'You're welcome, Annie. Have you eaten?'

She nodded. 'I'll make some coffee.'

'How about a bottle of that wine?'

She gave him a level look. 'I think not.'

He gave a wicked smile. 'I can't hide anything from

you, can I?' he said lightly, and turned back to the grill. 'Ah, well, I can take rejection when I have to.'

'You surprise me,' she said drily. 'I would have thought it was the first time you'd come up against it!'

He gave her a funny look. 'Not quite the first,' he murmured.

'Damn nearly.'

He chuckled. 'I'm flattered, but you're quite mistaken. I just wish I was so irresistible to you.'

He teased and bantered with her all through his meal, and Anne nursed her cup of coffee and thought how like old times it was—except that Beth was upstairs, a constant reminder of the time they had stepped over the invisible bounds of friendship.

She sent him home when he had finished eating, and after she had cleared up and locked the doors she made her way to bed.

As she leant over to close her curtains, she looked out and saw the car, a tangible reminder of his new role in her life.

She told herself it was for Beth, but as she lay in bed unable to sleep she heard his voice again telling her that they were both too precious to risk losing.

Whatever else he might have been, Jake had never been insincere. Despite her efforts to quell it, deep inside her a tiny flame of hope came to life. Did he really think she was precious? Perhaps, after all. . .

'Goodnight, Annie. Sleep well.'

She stamped firmly on the little flutter of her heart.

'Goodnight, Jake.'

The next day Mrs Partington was very uncomfortable and the volume of amniotic fluid had obviously increased, so she was taken to Theatre to have some of the fluid drawn off.

Using the ultrasound scanner to detect the position of the baby and the placenta, Jake selected the entry site for the large-bore needle that would permit the fluid to escape, and injected a local anaesthetic to numb the abdominal wall.

Once it had taken effect, he inserted the needle and very slowly and steadily, so as not to precipitate her labour, he withdrew nearly two litres of surplus fluid.

Mrs Partington was visibly relieved, and Anne was amazed at the vast amount of fluid he had been able to take off.

'Is that typical?' she asked later as they stripped off their theatre gowns.

'Oh, yes. The troubling thing is that she's quite likely to replace it within the next twenty-four hours, and we can't remove it on a daily basis—always assuming she doesn't go into labour anyway. We'll have to wait and see. If we can keep her hanging on another week, the baby'll be a lot stronger, but the danger is if her membranes rupture and the cord prolapses. She'll have to be watched very carefully. I think without doubt I'll do a section.'

They went back to the ward together, Jake to check on Mrs Partington, Anne to attend another forceps delivery.

The remainder of the week was busy, and they hardly saw each other during the day. On Friday Anne was held up with a protracted delivery, and when she rang Jenny to say she would be late she was told that Jake had already taken Beth home.

'Oh,' she said, totally nonplussed. 'Well, I'll pop in anyway with your cheque——'

'No need,' Jenny said airily. 'He's paid me already. I hope you didn't mind me handing her over, but he seemed quite happy—actually, Anne, I've been meaning to ask you about him——'

'Not now,' she said quickly, 'I'm in Theatre. I'll speak to you another time.'

Seething with rage at his interference in her business arrangement with the childminder, she finished off her delivery and drove home ready to kill.

There was a note on her door telling her that Beth was with him, and she leant on his doorbell until the door swung open.

'Did the bell stick?' he asked, puzzled.

'No, it didn't damn well stick. How dare you? Beth? Come here, darling, we're going home.'

He sighed and slouched back against the hall wall. 'What now, Annie?'

She whirled on him. 'What now? How dare you pay Jenny and take Beth away from her is what now. She's absolutely seething with curiosity as it is, and God knows what she thinks after this. You are the most arrogant, high-handed——'

'And you're being totally ridiculous. I knew you were going to be quite a bit later than you'd intended, and it seemed unfair to expect her to hang on to Beth without any warning——'

'She had warning! I rang her——'

'After I'd picked Beth up, I take it? What kind of a warning is that?'

Anne was furious. 'Perfectly adequate—we have an arrangement. If I'm going to be suddenly held up, she just carries on until I get there. She's used to it. It often happens, and she doesn't mind.'

Jake folded his arms and regarded her with infuriating calm.

'Are you sure?'

'Of course I'm sure—she'd tell me if she minded.

Next you'll be accusing me of taking advantage of
her—there you are, Beth. Get your things, darling,
and come now, please. You've got homework to
do——'

'I've done it. We were just going to cook some
pizzas—can't I stay, Mum?'

'No,' Anne snapped, 'you have to have a bath and
wash your hair before the morning. You'll have to have
pizza with Jake another night. Now come on.'

'Why don't I cook them while Beth has her bath,
and then bring them round in, say, half an hour?'

'Please, Mummy—please? I'll go to bed when you
tell me, only we've got mushrooms and prawns and
salami and all sorts of things on them——'

'It's enough to make you sick——'

'Spoilsport,' Jake said quietly, and she glared at him,
then opened her front door and sent Beth in before
turning back to him, her eyes flashing.

'Don't criticise me—especially not in front of my
daughter. Don't you dare think you can breeze back
into my life and throw your weight around like this!
It's bad enough that I've had to accept your charity
over the damn car without you interfering in every
other avenue of our lives!'

'You're beautiful when you're mad with me, do you
know that?'

She felt the angry prickle of tears and blinked hard.
'Damn it, Jake, listen to me! This is important!'

His hands came up and gripped her shoulders. She
got the distinct feeling he was tempted to shake her. 'I
know it's important, and I am listening to you, Annie,
but it's high time you listened to what I have to say.
There's a lot we need to sort out, starting with telling
Beth who I am. Go and bath her, and I'll be round

with the pizzas in half an hour. We'll talk after she's gone to bed.'

He released her and turned away, closing the door in her face.

Still shaking with anger and frustration, Anne went in through her own door, closed it and leant on it. She was going to have to face it in the end, she knew that, but he was pushing so hard for them to tell Beth, and after she was told would come all the questions.

'Why weren't you married?' 'Are you going to get married?' 'Why not?'

'Because he's a footloose playboy, and I don't have what it takes to hold him,' Anne said quietly to herself as she shrugged off her coat and flung it over the banisters.

Beth, intuitive as ever, was upstairs undressed and already running her bath. Her uniform was in the laundry basket, her schoolbag hung on the back of her door and she was being a perfect little cherub.

Anne wished she had a dog to kick. It would have made her feel only marginally worse.

'Sorry I was late,' she told her angelic daughter, and was rewarded with Jake's grin.

'That's OK. We had a great time. Jenny's friends came round because it was her birthday, and when Jake came over and said you'd be late she asked me if you'd mind him having me. I said no, so she asked him and he didn't mind, but you do, don't you?'

Anne stared at her blankly. 'Jenny asked Jake to have you? He didn't ask?'

'I said that—can I have bubble bath?'

'No, we have to wash your hair. What time was that?'

'Don't know. When he got back. Why can't I have bubble bath tonight and wash my hair tomorrow?'

'Because I say. Now get in and sit down.'

Beth pouted and climbed over the side of the bath. 'Why are you always so cross with Jake? He didn't mind, really, but you're so mad with him. I was only there for a little while, and he said he'd help me with my homework if I'd help him with the pizzas. He said he couldn't manage to decorate them by himself.'

Anne all but rolled her eyes. Trust Jake to play helpless. It was his favourite trick.

'I'm sure he can manage perfectly well without you,' she said tartly. 'Now let's do this hair.'

'Then can I have some bubble bath?'

Anne gritted her teeth. 'We'll see. Give me the shampoo.'

The doorbell rang before she had time to finish drying Beth's long, thick dark hair, so she handed Jake the hairdrier and brush and told him to do it while she washed and changed.

Let him have a sample of the nitty gritty, she thought, and he'll soon run.

She freshened up her make-up and pulled on jeans and a sweatshirt before running back downstairs.

Beth was sitting between Jake's feet on the floor while he patiently brushed out the tangles and smoothed it with the brush. When she went in he put down the hairdrier and brush and lifted the silky tresses back over Beth's shoulders, running his fingers through it experimentally.

'You've got beautiful hair, Beth,' he said quietly, and Anne had to look away from the expression on his face.

'Are the pizzas done?' she asked.

He sighed and stood up. 'They should be. I'll go and

get them, they're in my oven. How about a bottle of wine?'

Anne gave up fighting. He was right, they did have to talk, and anyway she owed him an apology over Jenny. Perhaps it would be easier if she wasn't stone-cold sober.

'Good idea. I'll come with you and give you a hand,' she told him. 'Beth, lay the table, please.'

She followed him out and ignored his raised eyebrows.

'Well? Spit it out.'

There was no point in beating about the bush. She took a deep breath. 'Beth told me Jenny asked you if you could have her.'

'That's right. I went over to tell her you'd be late and asked if it would be a problem, and she explained it was her birthday and she had friends there, and would I mind? I said of course not, and to save you going over and disturbing their evening with their friends when you got back I paid her. If it troubles you that much, you can pay me back, but for God's sake let's not have World War Three over it!'

'Oh.' There didn't seem much left to say, except sorry, and just then she felt it would choke her.

She met his eyes ruefully.

'Accepted,' he said with a grin. 'Now come on and let's get these pizzas out of the oven before they burn— and then we talk.'

CHAPTER SIX

THEY did talk—if you could call another acrimonious battle of wills talking.

Jake was adamant that they tell Beth who he was as soon as possible. Anne, knowing her daughter better than he did, thought they should leave it until she had returned from her grandparents' after half-term before they dropped a bombshell of that magnitude on her.

'I can't tell her something like that and then send her away, Jake! It wouldn't be fair.'

'It wouldn't be fair to let her find out from someone else, either. Have you thought of that? It's getting dangerous, Annie. Too many people know. I think Jenny's realised, and your friend Maggie was asking me some very searching questions the other day.'

'She knows,' Anne confirmed. 'She told me one lunchtime. She won't tell anyone, especially not this week. She's too busy planning the wedding. The only other people who know are my parents, and they certainly won't say anything to her.'

'She ought to know,' he insisted stubbornly. 'Damn it, it's her birthday on Sunday. Can you think of a better birthday present to give her than her father?'

'Oh, great!' Anne threw up her hands in the air and leapt to her feet. 'Fantastic! Can you imagine the questions? "When are you getting married? Why not?" She'll be impossible, Jake.'

'That's the crux of it, isn't it? You can't give the poor bloody kid a decent reason why we aren't getting married, because your excuses are too feeble to bear inspection! Damn it, Annie, I love you, and I love Beth, and I won't be thrust out into the cold like this! For God's sake, marry me and let's get this farce over with!'

She gave a short, bitter laugh. 'Is that how you see our relationship? A farce? Believe me, Jake, if we got married it would be. We've done nothing but fight since you came back into my life, and all because you won't pay any attention to my wishes!'

She whirled away from him, struggling to regain control of her shattered emotions. Taking a deep breath, she started again. 'You're crowding me, Jake, can't you understand? I've been alone for years making decisions and planning for the future with Beth, and then you—you bounce back like an enthusiastic puppy and expect everything to go your way! For God's sake, you aren't Peter Pan. When are you going to grow up and start to be sensible? Life isn't a game, Jacob. You can't treat my daughter's life like a prize to be won, and I'm damned if I'm going to spend years with you wondering what you're up to just so you can have easy access to Beth! I know you too well, Jake, and I won't be used by you as a bridge to our daughter, do you understand?'

He stared at her in disbelief for a few seconds, then shook his head slowly. 'Know me? I don't think you really have any idea who I am, do you? I'm not sure you ever did. I think you saw what you wanted to see, and ignored the rest. Even now you won't talk to me, you just say no to everything I suggest without giving it any consideration.'

'That's not true!' she protested. 'I've listened to everything you've said, but it all comes back to the same thing—for it to work, I have to be able to trust you. . .'

'And you can't.' He sighed and stood up, striding restlessly to the door. 'I'm wasting my breath, aren't I? I'll go and see a solicitor next week. It's time we sorted out something legal over maintenance and access. I had hoped we could handle this ourselves in the logical way, but you're obviously so prejudiced you'll never consider marriage to me.'

He ran his hands through his hair in a gesture of defeat. 'That's OK—I never really thought I had a chance with you, so I'll get used to it, but in the meantime we need to sort things out for Beth's sake. And I'll give you fair warning, Anne. If you don't tell her as soon as she gets back from your parents, then I will. She's waited long enough, and so have I.'

He let himself out quietly, and a few seconds later she heard him moving around in the sitting-room next door. It was too close, too intimate, and she went into the kitchen and made herself a cup of coffee, nursing it in trembling fingers.

He couldn't tell her—she simply wouldn't allow it! But how would she stop him? He wouldn't listen to her.

And will you listen to him? a little voice asked her. How would you feel in the same circumstances?

She was surprised at the jolt of pain she felt at the thought of not being able to acknowledge Beth. The only way that would really work for all of them was marriage, but her sensible, uncompromising nature wouldn't permit a gamble on Beth's happiness.

And what about yours and Jake's? the little voice interrupted again.

Anne sighed. He had sounded so defeated, but it wasn't as if she really mattered to him, not in that way.

He'd said he loved her, but he didn't mean it, not the way that it mattered. Not like she loved him.

Oh, God.

It hit her like a ton of bricks.

Surely, she told herself, after all this time she should have outgrown her childish infatuation for the larger-than-life hero he had been? He was just a playboy, a philanderer, unreliable, too busy chasing rainbows to settle down. How come he was available to take over from Jo at the drop of a hat? Where was his responsible job and mortgage and wife——? Well, she knew where his wife was.

Divorced, back in New York, abandoned.

But not her. Oh, no. She loved him. So what? Women had got over it before. She had once. She would again.

Setting down her mug in the sink, she made her way up to bed and lay for hours, staring at the ceiling in the dim light from the street lamps, listening for Jake in the room next door.

She couldn't miss it when he came to bed, the muffled curse as he obviously stubbed his toe, the creak of the bedsprings as he dropped on to the bed, his ragged sigh.

'Damn you, Annie,' he said, his voice slurred. 'Damn you to hell.'

She stifled the sob that rose in her throat. They were all caught in a trap and there seemed to be no way out, least of all for Beth.

And Anne knew, without a doubt, that their inno-cent and beautiful daughter would be the one to suffer most.

Saturday morning was quiet, mainly because it was raining heavily and the children weren't playing in the street as usual. Without their cries and laughter and the incessant ringing of bicycle bells, the place seemed empty.

Anne took Beth and went into town to buy a box of chocolates for Jenny, then nipped over to her house with it.

'Belgian chocs! Oh, you shouldn't—my diet!' Jenny wailed, and then licked her lips and grinned mischievously. 'Thanks, Anne. Bless you. Have you got time for a coffee?'

Beth had disappeared upstairs with Jenny's children, and they were alone in the kitchen.

'That would be lovely. As a matter of fact, I've been meaning to talk to you for days.'

Jenny shot her a shrewd look. 'About Jake?'

Anne sighed. 'Among other things.'

Jenny went to the sink to fill the kettle, and Anne's eyes strayed across the road. It had stopped raining, and Jake was washing his car, his powerful body moving easily and rhythmically as he reached across to wipe the bonnet. His jeans hugged his hips and legs with indecent familiarity, and she dragged her eyes away and went and sat down.

'Bit of a traffic-stopper, isn't he?' Jenny said over her shoulder as she plugged in the kettle. 'Same sort of startling good looks as Beth—hair, eyes. . .'

Anne sighed again, and Jenny sank down on the other side of the table and covered Anne's hand with her own. It was large and capable and work-roughened, and, like Jenny, it offered simple, undemanding comfort.

'It must be very difficult for you.'

'I haven't seen him for nearly eight years.'

Jenny released her hand and opened the chocolates, offering one to Anne. 'Why did you let him go? I'm damned if I would have done.'

Anne laughed. 'You don't let Jake go, Jenny. He just takes off when he's ready.'

'Did he know you were pregnant?'

Anne shook her head. 'No. Not until later. He thought she was someone else's until he saw her on Monday.'

Jenny bit the tail off a chocolate seahorse and eyed Anne over the top. 'It must have been a hell of a shock when he turned up out of the blue. Is there any likelihood of you getting married?'

'No.' She shook her head wearily. 'No, Jen. No chance. He says he wants to, but I know him too well. It's only because it's a challenge. Once we settled down to the humdrum nitty gritty, he'd be bored stiff in ten seconds flat!' She drew a circle in a puddle of spilt milk on the table-top with her finger. 'He thinks we should tell Beth. I don't agree.'

Jenny eyed her thoughtfully. 'She talks about him constantly, you know. Jake's done this, Jake's done that. She told me about the car. She also told me she's caught you kissing.'

Anne blushed furiously. 'It was a mistake,' she muttered.

'Kissing him, or being caught by Beth?'

'Both! Oh, God, Jenny, I don't know what to do for the best. I'm so worried she'll be hurt, and yet I know perfectly well if we get married and it goes wrong she'll be hurt far worse than if we carry on as we are.'

'And what about you?' Jenny asked gently. 'What do you want?'

Anne met her searching eyes, and looked quickly away. 'I want him to vanish so we can forget about him.'

The kettle boiled, and Jenny stood up to make the coffee. 'I don't think you're being very realistic,' she said pragmatically as she sat down again. 'He's not going anywhere, I wouldn't have said. When I asked him last night if he could take her, his eyes lit up as if he'd won the pools! And Beth was over the moon. I hate to say it, Anne, but those two have fallen for each other in a big way this week. You try and cut him out of her life, and you'll have problems on your hands.'

She sighed and stirred her coffee absently. 'I can't cut him out, I know that, but how far do I dare to let him in? If only I could trust him it would be so simple!'

'You can trust him with Beth, I'm sure of that.'

'I have no choice,' Anne said drily. 'He's going to a solicitor to get some legal advice about access and things.' She sipped her coffee, and set it down again. 'I don't suppose I could ask you a favour, could I? Would you keep an eye on Beth for an hour so I can get to town and get her a birthday present? I meant to do it this week, but somehow I haven't been able to concentrate. . .'

'Oh, Anne, I'm sorry—any other time, but as soon as Phil gets back from town we're off to his parents for the day. I'd love to say yes, but today is just impossible. I'm sorry. Why not ask Jake?'

Anne laughed. 'Are you mad? I'd rather take her with me!'

'That's pointless, and anyway, don't you think they have a right to be alone together?'

The silence hummed with Jenny's gentle reproach.

Anne stood up and put her cup in the sink. 'Of course they do. I'll ask him. And I'm sorry about last night.'

'Think nothing of it. I just hope you didn't mind me handing her over to someone else like that, but in the circumstances. . .'

Anne gave a tiny laugh. 'Forget it, Jen. Have a

lovely day out, and I'll see you after next week, if not before.' She called Beth back downstairs, and together they walked back across the road, Beth skipping and dancing on the end of Anne's arm.

Jake was outside still, polishing his car now.

'Mummy, there's Jake!' Beth said excitedly, and, slipping her hand out of Anne's, she ran over to him and gave him a big hug.

'Hello, sweetheart,' he said gently, and hugged her back.

'Can I do that?'

He handed her the polishing cloth and straightened up slowly.

Anne walked up to him, her eyes scanning his features. He look awful—whether from lack of sleep or the alcohol he'd obviously drunk last night, she wasn't sure.

'Good morning,' he said, his voice carefully expressionless.

'Good morning. Jake, I wonder if I could ask a favour. I need to go shopping—alone,' she explained quietly. 'I wondered if you would mind looking after Beth for me for a while?'

'Are you sure you trust me?' he asked bitterly, and turned away. 'Of course I'll have her—here, Tuppence, what would you like to do this morning? Your mother has to go out, so we've got lots of time. Got any ideas?'

'I'll leave you my back door key as well, so you can get in and out for boots and things for her.'

She left them plotting their morning and went in and got the key.

'Are you sure it's OK?' she asked once more.

'Of course—and don't worry, Annie. I'll look after her.'

She nodded silently and kissed Beth goodbye. 'I'll see you later—I'll be back for lunch. Be good.'

It didn't take her long—she knew exactly where to find the luminous pink and green roller boots Beth had begged and pleaded for. She got her a larger size to give her plenty of wear, and then found herself unable to resist the bright pink Lycra leggings that went so well with them.

The rain had started again, and she ran back to the car. It was only just after twelve when she got back, and they were nowhere to be seen, so she took advantage of Beth's absence to wrap her present and hide it in the top of her wardrobe.

By one o'clock she had prepared lunch for all of them and was beginning to worry when Jake's car swept on to the drive and he and Beth tumbled out, filthy dirty and giggling like children—which she could forgive Beth, but as for Jake. . .it was only what she had come to expect.

They came to the back door, and Jake handed Beth over with a rakish grin.

'I've made lunch,' she said with a disapproving look at his filthy jeans.

'For me?'

She nodded. 'If you want it.'

'I'll just go and clean up—give me two minutes.'

He was back in five, by which time she had managed to prise Beth out of her stinking ski-pants and had got her in the bath.

'Up here,' Anne yelled when she heard the back door shut.

He followed the noise upstairs and found them in the bathroom.

Beth was in the bath, telling Anne all about falling

over in the mud at Walberswick and seeing the heron and how the swans had chased them over the mud flats.

'I fell over again,' she said cheerfully.

'I would never have guessed,' Anne replied drily, shoving up her sleeves and scrubbing the mucky child. 'How did you get it in your hair?' she asked in despair. 'Lie down, let me wash it.' She screwed round and peered up at Jake. 'You needn't look so pleased with yourself. Are you clean?'

His grin widened. 'Just about. Want a hand?'

She stood up. 'You want to be a parent—you do it,' she muttered under her breath. 'And try not to get shampoo in her eyes.'

She left them together, which she realised almost immediately was another mistake.

She could tell from the splashing and giggling that the bathroom would be awash by the time she got back in there, but she couldn't be bothered to fight.

'Her clean clothes are on her bed,' she said through the door. 'I'll be downstairs when you've finished.'

She went down and rescued the pasta bake from the oven, and then waited, listening in resignation to the muffled shrieks of laughter from the bathroom overhead.

After a minute or two they moved to Beth's bedroom, and within a short while they appeared, her daughter's hair roughly towelled dry, her face shiny and pink and her clothes on, apparently in the right order.

Jake, on the other hand, was drenched.

She suppressed a smile.

'How are the water babies? Ready for lunch?'

They both nodded enthusiastically.

'I'm starving,' Jake confessed.

'Me too. We walked miles. Jake's very good at birdwatching.'

Anne's smile broke free. 'It's all the practice he gets,' she said with mock innocence, ignoring his splutter of protest.

He disappeared soon after lunch, taking his car out and acting evasive. Anne hoped he wasn't going to do something silly and buy the entire contents of a toy shop for Beth.

After Anne had done some washing so that Beth would have a few clean clothes to take away with her the next day, they sat in the sitting-room, staring through the patio doors at the relentless rain.

'We were going to build a snowman for my birthday,' Beth said sadly.

'Never mind, poppet. Perhaps we can find something else to do. Would you like to play a game?'

They got a couple of games out of the cupboard and spent the next hour or so on the floor in front of the gas fire until Beth was bored again.

Anne usually found it easy to entertain Beth, but today, for some reason, she found it impossibly difficult to concentrate. If only the weather was nice and they could go out somewhere, she thought, and then acknowledged that if it was brilliant sunshine and hot enough to fry eggs they'd still be at home because what they were actually doing, consciously or not, was waiting for Jake.

When he did come back he let himself into his house, ran upstairs and then came back down and rang the doorbell. They listened to his progress, and as the bell rang, Beth ran to let him in.

'You're wet—come in and get dry by the fire.'

'Thank you, Beth,' he said with only the faintest

trace of humour. He hung his coat over the banisters and went into the sitting-room.

'Playing Scrabble?' he said to Anne.

Beth nodded. 'Mummy always wins,' she said dolefully.

Jake grinned. 'Not always.' He met Anne's eyes, his own warm with the memory of wet Sunday afternoons spent by the fire playing Scrabble or Monopoly. 'Fancy a game?'

'With you? No way. You always win!'

Suddenly breathless at the look in his eyes, she scrambled to her feet and tugged her sweatshirt down, running her fingers over her hair to tame it.

'Cup of tea?'

'If I may.' He followed her into the kitchen, suddenly diffident. 'I don't want to outstay my welcome, Anne.'

'Don't be silly, Jake. Provided you aren't trying to coerce me into marriage, you're more than welcome. In fact, you can do me a favour and go and entertain Beth.'

'Right.' He left the kitchen, and a few moments later she heard his deep voice rumbling from the sitting-room, and Beth's high-pitched, excited giggle.

Suddenly he roared, and Beth shrieked, and they both collapsed in a fit of giggles.

In the kitchen, Anne felt suddenly, ridiculously left out. So he was telling his daughter a story. So what? Why should she feel—good heavens!—jealous?

She sat down abruptly at the table. It was still less than a week since he'd strolled into their lives. Surely to God things would get better?

As sure as eggs is eggs, she thought, they can't get any worse!

* * *

Sunday dawned cold, wet, and much too early.

Beth was up slightly before the lark, bouncing into Anne's bedroom and climbing into bed with her.

'Happy Birthday, sweetheart,' Anne said sleepily, and wrapped her arms round her daughter's wriggling body.

She snuggled closer and slipped her arms round Anne. 'When can I get up and open my presents?' she asked after a few restless minutes.

Anne gave a resigned laugh.

'Would you like them now?'

'Yes, please!' Beth bounced up in the bed and grinned.

Good grief, Anne thought, if her tongue lolled she'd be a puppy!

Throwing off the bedclothes, she pulled on her robe and wrapped it firmly round her middle.

'In the sitting-room,' she said, and followed Beth down the stairs more sedately.

By the time she got there Beth had already torn the wrapper off her roller boots and was dragging them out of the box.

'Oh, Mum, they're ace! Thanks! And leggings—wow!'

She flung herself into Anne's arms and hugged her, just as the doorbell rang.

Wriggling out of her mother's grasp, she flew down the hall and yanked open the door.

'Happy Birthday!' Jake yelled, and Beth threw herself into his arms. He picked her up and whirled her round, hugging her little body close to his chest and laughing with delight, and then finally set her down with a big smacking kiss.

'How's my birthday girl?' he asked her.

She peered curiously round him. 'What's that?'

'What——? Oh, that! I don't know—had we better look?'

She giggled. 'It's a present.'

'No—really? Well, upon my soul! So it is—here, you'd better open it as you're the birthday girl.' He straightened up and smiled tentatively at Anne. 'I hope you don't mind—I heard you up.'

She made herself smile. 'Of course I don't mind—it's a special day. What have you got there, darling?'

She was relieved to see only the one present—goodness knew he'd been gone long enough yesterday.

However, it was obviously more than a token gesture. Beth was struggling with a parcel nearly her own size.

'Here, let me,' Jake said, and, taking it from her, he went into the sitting-room.

There Beth shredded the wrapping paper and shrieked with delight. 'It's a Scalextric! Oh, magic, Jake, thank you!'

She threw herself into his arms, and over her head Jake met Anne's astonished gaze.

'I'll make some tea while you set it up,' she said, and went into the kitchen to get away from him.

Her heart was going nineteen to the dozen, and she plugged in the kettle and stood staring out of the window, gripping the edge of the sink as if it was her sanity.

He had obviously just crawled out of bed, and where she looked a total mess he looked rumpled and deliciously sexy. His jaw was rough with stubble, his jeans tugged on above bare feet, his shirt half undone and open at the neck to show off the soft tangle of curls that nestled on his chest.

Her fingers twitched with the remembered feel of it beneath her palms.

'Are you OK?'

He was right behind her, and she jumped.

'I was fine till you sneaked up on me.' She turned and looked him dead in the eye. 'Toy racing cars?'

He shrugged sheepishly. 'That's what she likes to play with at Jenny's. She said the other day she'd love a set but they were probably too expensive.'

Anne's mouth straightened repressively. 'Yes, well, I'm inclined to agree with her.'

He gave a crooked smile. 'There was so much I wanted to buy her, and I knew you'd go AWOL if I came back with half the shop. In fact, you should be commending me for my restraint!'

'Congratulations,' she said drily, suddenly aware of the nearness of his body and the tantalising, masculine scent that drifted to her on his warmth.

Their eyes meshed, the awareness humming between them like electricity.

'You look wonderful,' he murmured, 'soft and warm and rumpled.'

Her breath caught in her throat. She swallowed hard and her tongue flicked out to moisten her suddenly dry lips.

His breath hissed out sharply. 'God, Annie, don't do that,' he growled softly. His eyes tracked over the gaping front of her dressing-gown, and she clutched the edges together and turned away.

'I wasn't expecting visitors at this hour,' she told him. She tried to sound repressive, but her voice betrayed her and her words came out on a breathy sigh.

His hands closed over her shoulders, pulling her back against him. His body felt lean and hard, warm, and very, very masculine.

She pulled away from him before her knees collapsed.

'No,' she said, her voice rough and edgy. 'Jake, please. It isn't fair.'

'All's fair in love and war, Annie.'

She turned to face him. 'Not this war, Jake. There's a child involved.'

On cue the child appeared in the doorway and seized Jake by the hand. 'Will you help me? I can't do it by myself.'

Shooting her a look that promised their discussion was far from over, he followed Beth back into the sitting-room, leaving Anne alone, her emotions in turmoil.

How could she hope to keep him at a distance if her traitorous body leapt to life every time he looked at her?

Well, thank God her parents were coming to tea this afternoon and would take Beth away for a week. Then he'd have no excuse to see her—and, her little voice reminded her, she'd have no built-in reason to call a halt.

Her heart pounded, she thought at first with fear, but then she became aware of the clamouring of her body and knew it wasn't fear at all, but longing.

CHAPTER SEVEN

DESPITE the state of nervous anticipation in which Anne found herself, it was a wonderful day. Jake set up the winding race-track on the sitting-room floor, and he taught Beth how to race the little electric cars, her small hand engulfed in his much larger one as he showed her how much pressure to apply to the trigger, and how to control the speed on the bends so that her car didn't fly off the track as it so often did.

For a while Anne curled up on the sofa and watched them, their faces so alike as they concentrated fiercely on the race.

Then Jake's car spun off on the bend and Beth won the race, shrieking with delight and bouncing up and down.

Jake looked up and met Anne's raised eyebrow with a wicked wink, and they shared an indulgent smile.

God forbid that Beth should realise he had let her win, Anne thought, stifling her smile as Beth turned to her.

'Did you see?' she asked excitedly.

Anne laughed, suddenly conscious of an overwhelming happiness. 'Yes, darling, I saw. Well done.'

She stood up and straightened her dressing-gown, ignoring Jake's blatant appraisal of her legs as she moved.

'I'm going to get dressed,' she announced.

'Good idea,' he said, rising easily to his bare feet. He followed her into the hall. 'Is there a roller-skating rink open on Sundays near here?' he asked softly, so that Beth wouldn't hear.

'Yes, I think the one in Bury is. Why?'

He shrugged. 'I thought she'd like to go. Would that be OK?'

'She'd love it—I hadn't even thought of it. The only problem is, I can't skate and I wouldn't like her going on there with all those teenagers without someone with her.'

'That's OK,' he assured her. 'I can skate—or I used to be able to. I'm sure I haven't forgotten.'

She met his eyes. 'My parents are coming for tea, so we need to be back soon after lunch, but we could go this morning. I'll ring Jenny—she'll know if they're open.'

'Fine.' The tension sizzled between them again, until with a visible effort he drew away from her. 'I'll see you at nine.'

'OK.'

She watched him go, then ran lightly upstairs and showered and dressed, dimly aware that she was humming under her breath but unwilling to stamp on the little bubble of joy inside her.

They were doing this for Beth, she reminded herself, but that didn't mean she had to hate it. She had always enjoyed Jake's company, and it surely wasn't wrong if she still did?

The rink was indeed open on Sundays, she was told, so she dressed Beth in her new leggings and a sloppy sweatshirt and put the boots by the door.

On the dot of nine Jake rang the doorbell, reminding her that for all his faults he had always been reliable about timekeeping, and they set off, Beth bubbling happily in the back of Jake's car.

'I like Mummy's new car, but this is much nicer,' she told Jake confidentially.

'It should be,' Anne commented drily. 'It cost a great deal more!'

'Are you rich?' Beth asked him curiously, craning her neck to see his face.

His lips twitched. 'Not really. I was richer before I bought the car.'

'Oh,' she said, obviously disappointed.

Anne had to smile.

'Talking of cars,' Jake added, turning to Anne, 'yesterday afternoon I called at the garage where you bought your old wreck. If we take the car back, they'll give you your money back.'

Anne's mouth fell open in astonishment. 'How on earth did you persuade them to agree to that?' she asked, amazed.

He grinned wickedly. 'Let's just say they were amenable to reason.'

'You mean you threatened them?'

The grin widened. 'Would I?'

She laughed. 'You would. I've seen you in action before, Hunter. You're totally unscrupulous.'

'Not totally. Once you've got your money back, I intend to report them to the police. They're obviously running a racket there, and I think in the interests of public safety they should be stopped.'

Was this a new Jake, or had he always been so public-spirited? She honestly wasn't sure, so she had to give him the benefit of the doubt. It was a sobering thought.

Beth chattered all the way to Bury, and when they went into the skating rink, her happiness overflowed.

Anne laced her into the new boots while Jake put on

his hired ones, and then he helped her to her feet and led her carefully on to the wooden floor.

Skating backwards, he held her hands to steady her and guided her slowly round the rink while Anne sat by the side and watched them through the colourful throng.

Gradually she gained confidence, and after about an hour she was skating alone beside Jake, laughing happily up into his face, her own flushed with a mixture of exertion and joy.

This was what she had missed all these years, Anne thought with a pang of regret. A father to look up to, to do the things that fathers did so well and that mothers could only hope to imitate.

And she had missed out, too—missed out on the shared moments of their daughter's progress, the laughter and the tears, the warmth, the passion.

The pang of regret for the past they had lost became a deep, gnawing ache of longing for the future she knew they could never share.

'Damn you, Jacob Hunter,' she whispered. 'Why can't I hate you?'

Her eyes continued to follow them until, finally exhausted, they skated to the edge of the rink and came and sat beside her.

'Well done, darling, that was super,' she said warmly, hugging her daughter close. 'Clever girl.'

'Jake's brilliant!' Beth told her. 'Did you see him? He can go really fast, and turn round and everything!'

Her eyes were wide with wonder and hero-worship, and Anne forced a smile. If he ever lets her down, she thought, I'll kill him. I'll go after him and find him and tear him limb from limb——

'Contemplating murdering someone?' he said softly in her ear.

She laughed a little off key. 'How did you guess? Come on, let's go. I'm dying for a coffee and I expect you are, too.'

'Can we go to a Happy Eater?'

She opened her mouth to protest, but shut it again. It *was* Beth's birthday, after all. So what if she couldn't really afford it?

Jake quirked an eyebrow. 'My treat?'

She crumbled under their hopeful looks.

'That would be lovely. Thank you, Jake.'

'Great! Fantastic! Mum, what time are Grannie and Grandpa coming over?'

'About three, so we'd better get going because I have to make sandwiches.'

They arrived back shortly after two, and while Beth played with her Scalextric, Anne and Jake made sandwiches in her tiny kitchen—which meant they were forever falling over each other. In the end she sat him down with a pile of bread to butter and concentrated on making the fillings.

'Do you want me to go before your parents arrive?' he asked her quietly.

She stopped mashing the hard-boiled eggs and met his eyes frankly. 'No. They have to know you're back in our lives, and I'd like them to see you with Beth, so they know they can trust you.'

'Even though you can't?'

She flushed. 'You were a good friend, Jake. I'm just hoping you'll take the same role with Beth as you did with me.'

He gave a humourless little laugh. 'Not entirely the same role, I hope?'

'Well, obviously not that——'

She stopped abruptly, and attacked the eggs as if her life depended on it. 'You know what I mean.'

His mouth twisted into a parody of a smile. 'It's all right, Anne. I won't let her down—or you, although I know you don't believe me. Maybe time will prove you wrong.'

He stood up. 'I'll go and change into something more appropriate for meeting my daughter's grandparents.'

She flicked an eye over him. 'You look fine.'

'Thank you, but I'm not trying to please you. It's called power-dressing, Annie. Believe me, I'm going to need all the ammunition I can produce.'

'Rubbish. They've never said a word against you, Jake.'

'To you. I doubt if they'll show the same reserve with me.' He paused in the doorway. 'I know it's a lot to ask, but it would help to know you were on my side.'

She put down the fork and turned to face him. 'I'm on Beth's side, Jake, and I know you love her. That's enough for me.'

'I love you, too, you know.'

'That's a different issue.'

'Is it?'

The look in his eyes was more than she could cope with. If she allowed herself, she could almost believe. . . She wiped her hands on a towel and started filling the sandwiches.

'Yes, it is. Please, Jake. . .'

He sighed and threw up his hands. 'OK, OK. I'll be back in a minute.'

While he was changing, she ran upstairs and packed Beth's clothes in a little holdall. There were pitifully few things that still fitted her, Anne thought with a sigh.

Perhaps her mother would take her out during the week and kit her out with some more ski-pants and sweatshirts. She would certainly need them if Jake was going to take her on many more expeditions like yesterday's!

The packing done, she ran back downstairs and opened a packet of biscuits and some little fancy cakes. Her mother was bringing the birthday cake, as Anne hadn't had time to make one this year. It was the first time, and had she had less on her plate she might have minded, but as it was she was simply grateful.

As she filled the kettle at the sink, her parents pulled up outside the house.

'Beth,' she called, 'Grannie and Grandpa are here.'

Footsteps thundered down the hall and the door crashed back on its hinges as Beth flew out into the front garden.

Her grandfather scooped her up and hugged her, then set her down and looked around at the cars.

Anne followed her daughter out into the garden and kissed her father's cheek.

'Hello, Pop.'

'Hello, darling. New neighbours?'

'He's called Jake,' Beth burst in, 'and he's bought Mummy a new car, and he gave me a Scalextric for my birthday, and—here he is! Jake, come and say hello to Grandpa.'

Anne's father's face creased into a frown. 'Jake?' he said, glancing from the smartly dressed man in front of him to his dumb-struck daughter. Jake had changed out of his jeans and pullover into a pair of smart trousers, a shirt and tie and a lovat green sports coat. He looked, she thought numbly, deceptively respect-able—and decidedly sexy at the same time.

She found her voice. 'You remember Jacob Hunter, Dad. I trained with him.'

Jake stepped forward, his hand outheld. 'Mr Gabriel.'

Her father ignored his hand, until Beth made it impossible for him to do so.

'He's waiting to shake hands with you, Grandpa!' she said in a stage whisper, and Mr Gabriel had no alternative but to extend his own hand and grip Jake's briefly.

Anne made herself look at her mother, and encountered her shocked stare with as much calm as she could muster.

'Mum, you remember Jake, don't you? He's covering for Jo Harding—Carter now.'

Her mother pulled herself together with a visible effort and approached Jake with a polite social smile.

'Of course I remember—hello, Jake.' She held out her hand and took his without hesitation. 'What a surprise!'

He met her eyes steadily. 'Yes, it was, but a wonderful one nevertheless.'

Their eyes strayed to Beth, busy showing her grandfather the new car.

'She doesn't know yet,' Anne said quietly. 'We'll tell her next week. We didn't think it was a good idea to tell her and then send her away.'

'Quite,' Mrs Gabriel said, her eyes on Beth. 'Jake, there are some things in the boot of the car—perhaps you'd be kind enough to bring them in.'

She steered Anne through the door into the kitchen, and pushed the door shut.

'What on earth is he doing here?'

Anne shrugged. 'Jo fixed it—she doesn't realise about Beth, of course, but I think she was probably matchmaking.'

'Dear God—darling, are you all right? It must have come as a terrible shock. You might have warned us!'

'I'm sorry—I didn't know quite how to put it,' she explained lamely. 'My feelings have been turned upside-down this week.'

'What about Jake? How does he feel?'

'Oh, God, Mum, he wants to marry me.'

'Oh, dear. How do you feel about that?'

'I don't know—confused.'

Jake put his head round the door. 'Do you want the cake in here?'

'Yes—are the others coming in?'

He gave a rueful grin. 'I think your father would rather not be in the house with me,' he told Anne.

'Rubbish,' Mrs Gabriel said, straightening her shoulders. 'What's done is done. This is Beth's birthday, and I won't have it ruined because of his outdated moral outrage.'

She went to the door. 'Matthew? Bring that child inside out of the cold and let's have a look at these presents here.'

'Presents?' Beth squealed, and darted back in through the door, leaving her grandfather to follow reluctantly.

'I hardly feel——' he began, but his wife cut him off.

'This is not a time for what you feel. Now, Beth, let's go in the sitting-room.'

They moved away from the kitchen door, and Jake closed his eyes and leant against the wall, rubbing his hands over his face.

'I knew it would be grim,' he said heavily. 'Perhaps I should go away?'

'And look guilty? That's the last thing you should do. You look very respectable, by the way.'

He gave a half-hearted grin. 'It hasn't worked.'

She smiled reassuringly. 'It has on my mother! Come on, let's go and get this over with.'

The afternoon was stiff and difficult for everyone except Beth, who was so busy with her presents that she hardly noticed the adults at all.

As if to separate Anne and Jake, Anne's parents had taken up residence at each end of the sofa, thus forcing the other two to sit on the chairs at opposite ends of the room, and leaving a space for Beth in the middle. She bounced on and off the sofa intermittently, in between playing with her toys and dragging Jake down on to the floor with her to demonstrate her racing cars.

'Hardly a girl's toy,' Matthew Gabriel said repressively, but Beth disagreed.

'It's terrific—I love it! Look, see if I can beat Jake again—there! He came off! You went too fast, Jake!'

He set down the control and ruffled her hair. 'You're too good for me, cotton-top. I obviously need more practice.'

She giggled delightedly. 'Don't worry, Jake, I'll teach you!'

He chuckled. 'Cheeky monkey—come and give me a cuddle for losing.'

Beth swarmed up into his lap and snuggled down against him.

Anne watched her father stiffen, and immediately asked him to help her bring out the food. Once in the kitchen, he opened his mouth and found her finger pointing directly at it.

'Not a word, Pop. He's her father, whatever the rights and wrongs of it. Let me deal with it, please.'

They put the sandwiches and cakes on the coffee-table, and when her grandmother patted the seat between her and her husband Beth dutifully sat on it to eat her tea, and then blew out her candles.

While they were all singing 'Happy Birthday', Anne glanced up and saw Jake's face taut with feeling, and her eyes misted. She normally found it a fairly moving occasion. How much more so for Jake, doing this for the first time?

Filled with importance, Beth cut the cake, gave everybody a slice and then took hers over to Jake, climbing on to his knee again.

'Lovely cake, Mum,' Anne said to fill the pregnant silence.

'I like the jam inside,' Beth said. 'We had hot doughnuts for breakfast the other day—they were all jammy. Jake had three.'

You could have cut the tension with a knife.

Anne blushed, her father spluttered into his tea and had to mop himself up with a handkerchief, and Mrs Gabriel looked from Jake to Anne and back, her face a picture.

But Beth wasn't finished.

'I wish you were here for breakfast every day,' she said wistfully. 'Then you'd be like a daddy. I haven't got a daddy—not a proper one.' She met his stunned eyes, her own wide and innocent, and her jammy little hand reached up and touched his cheek. 'I wish you were my daddy, Jake.'

There was a shocked silence, and everyone held their breath. After an endless moment, Jake closed his eyes and wrapped his arms round her in a fierce hug. His voice was gruff. 'Believe me, darling, nothing would make me prouder than to be able to call you my daughter.'

Anne pressed her hand to her lips, her heart breaking at the raw emotion etched on Jake's features.

Then he opened his eyes and looked straight at her, the hurt clearly visible.

'If you'll all excuse me, I think I'll be going now.'

He pressed a kiss on Beth's hair and slid her off his lap to the floor. 'Have a lovely time, poppet. I'll see you next week.'

Anne leapt up. 'I'll show you out.'

Her mother quickly rose to her feet and knelt on the floor beside Beth. 'Show me how to race these cars, Beth,' she said firmly.

Anne and Jake escaped into the hall, and without a word she held out her arms and hugged him.

'I'm sorry,' she whispered. 'Are you all right?'

'I'll live,' he said, his voice ragged. 'Annie, I have to get out of here. Let me go, love, please.'

But Anne's father was too quick for them.

'A word, young man,' he said, closing the sitting-room door behind them. 'My daughter and my grand-daughter mean the world to me. I thought we'd seen the last of you seven years ago, but I was obviously wrong. But you mark my words—if you hurt them, you'll have me to deal with. I don't want you in my daughter's life, messing it up again like you did before——'

'Fortunately it's none of your damn business,' Jake said roughly, and, wrenching open the door, he ran through the rain and got into his car, gunning the engine and shooting off the drive in a squeal of tyres.

'Shocking way to drive.'

Anne thought so, too, but more because she was worried about Jake than because she thought his driving was inappropriate.

She turned on her father. 'Why did you have to say that? Couldn't you see he was upset?'

'And what do you think we've been all these years,

watching you being shamed and humiliated because of his careless behaviour? In my day a man took care of that side of things, but these days it strikes me anything goes!'

'It was my behaviour too, Dad.'

'And that's another thing—what's all this about breakfast?'

Anne could have told him the truth, but she was so angry with him she didn't bother.

'Mind your own damn business,' she said sharply, echoing Jake's words, and went back into the sitting-room.

'We'll be on our way now, darling,' her mother said. 'Are Beth's things ready?'

'They're in the hall.' She helped Beth into her coat, gave her a big kiss and a hug, and then kissed her mother. 'Look after her for me.'

'I will. And don't worry. I have a feeling about this.'

She grimaced. 'So does Dad. Try and talk him down, eh?'

'I'll do my best. Right, Beth, let's get you home and see what we can find to entertain you this week!' She hefted the little holdall. 'Is this everything?'

Anne shrugged. 'She grew.'

Her mother smiled understandingly. 'Beth, you and I are going shopping—won't that be fun?'

Anne watched them drive away, and then cleared up the tea things. She packed up the racing cars, cleared away the wrapping paper and vacuumed the floor, washed up the plates and cups and put them away, stripped Beth's bed and remade it and went back downstairs.

There was still no sign of Jake, and by ten she was worried sick.

At ten-thirty he drove back, considerably more

slowly than he had left, and walked wearily up the path.

He was drenched, his hair plastered down against his scalp, his shirt and jacket soaked. He was shivering with cold.

'Where've you been?' she asked gently.

He shrugged. 'Just—walking around. I'm sorry I drove off like that. I was angry and upset.'

'It's OK, I understand. Go and get changed into something warm and come back. I'll fix you a drink.'

He shook his head. 'I don't think so. I'm still very angry—I'm not sure I trust myself alone with you at the moment.' His hand curled into a fist and he slammed it into the wall, oblivious to the pain.

'Damn it, Annie, you had no right to keep us apart all this time—no right at all! She needs me—if you could have felt the tension in her when she said——' His voice cracked and he dropped his head against the wall. 'Oh, God, all those wasted years. . .'

She could hear the tears that clogged his throat, but he was still rigid with tension, and she wasn't sure how much it would take for him to snap.

'Sit down while I get you a glass of wine,' she suggested.

He rolled wearily against the wall until his back was against it and he was facing her.

'I don't want a glass of wine,' he said emphatically. 'I want my daughter—our daughter. I want a home and a marriage and—happy ever after.'

He laughed a little crazily.

'I don't want much, do I? But you could give it to me, all of it, if you would only take the risk. But you won't, will you? Oh, no. You've got to play it safe, as usual. What happened on finals night, Annie? You took a risk then, didn't you?'

'Yes,' she said quietly. 'And look where it got me. I think you should go home now, Jake.'

'I think that would be a very good idea. I don't think my self-control's what it ought to be, and the way I feel right now I'm not sure if I want to strangle you or take you to bed.' Shouldering himself away from the wall, he brushed a cool, rain-damp kiss on her forehead. 'Goodnight, princess. I'll see you tomorrow.'

She watched him go, his shoulders still rigid with anger, and could have wept for him, and for Beth, and for the mess they were all in. Had she been wrong all those years? Should she have told him?

No, of course not, because the man he had been was not a man to take the responsibility of parenthood.

And now? He could so easily have told Beth. Perhaps he had changed—and perhaps she was wrong about him, after all. . .

The following week was filled with tension. Jake was avoiding her, but their work thrust them together repeatedly, and the contact was bitter-sweet.

On Wednesday morning Mrs Partington had to go back to Theatre to have more fluid drawn off, and by eleven o'clock it was apparent that the procedure had triggered her body into premature labour.

'She'll have to have a section,' Jake told Annie. 'I don't want to risk any head injuries with a vaginal delivery when the baby's going to have to undergo surgery in the first few hours, and he's still six weeks prem. I'll get on the blower to Great Ormond Street so they're ready to receive it, and I'll get a paediatrician up here and the ambulance on standby with an incubator. How do you fancy doing the op?'

'Me?'

'Why not? Have you done any sections?'

She shrugged slightly. 'Yes; I've assisted Alex and Jo with several, and I've done two under Alex's watchful eye, but they were very routine—nothing like this. One was a pelvic disproportion and the other a placenta praevia.'

He chuckled. 'This is no different—just a little wetter! And you have to work fast in case the cord prolapses if the membranes tear as you go in, but if we get most of the fluid off beforehand it shouldn't feel very different from routine.'

Anne was still doubtful. 'Will she be conscious?'

Jake nodded. 'If we can get an anaesthetist to give her an epidural in time; that way she'll get to see her baby before it's whisked away for surgery.' He gave her shoulder a reassuring squeeze. 'I'll be there—I can take over if necessary, but I'm sure it won't be. Alex says you're very good, and I've seen nothing to make me doubt that.'

He went into Sister's office to use the phone, and left her standing in the corridor, glowing with pride at his simple praise.

Until then she hadn't realised just how much his approval mattered to her.

Under his skilful direction, she found herself drawing off as much amniotic fluid as possible before making the first incision, but as she proceeded her confidence grew.

'Right,' Jake said as she was about to enter the uterus. 'It could get a little wet round here now.'

She took a deep breath to steady her hands and made the incision.

A huge spurt of amniotic fluid shot up in the air. Jake ducked and there was a muffled shriek from behind him.

'Suction, please, I think,' Jake said with laughter in

his voice, and turned to wink at the saturated circulating nurse behind him.

'OK?'

'I will be when I change,' she said ruefully.

Stifling her laughter, Anne apologised and quickly completed the delivery.

The baby boy, slippery but very much alive, was lifted out and over the green drapes, to be placed in Mrs Partington's waiting arms.

'Oh, he's lovely!' she said tearfully, and Jake winked at Anne.

'Told you,' he said under his breath. 'Now you can get her sorted out at your own speed. Peter, he's all yours.'

Peter Travers, the consultant paediatrician, was already at the head of the table, running skilful hands over the baby.

'Lovely job,' he said with satisfaction. 'Good, strong young man we've got here. Can't see any problems—right, Mrs Partington, I'm afraid we're going to have to take him away from you, because this operation has to be done very quickly, but in a couple of days when you're feeling more the thing you'll be transferred to Great Ormond Street so you'll be able to see him. You'll be amazed at how quickly you're both over this and on the mend.'

She nodded, kissed her tiny son and watched helplessly as he was wheeled away in a heated cot.

'He'll be fine,' Jake said comfortingly. 'We'll get you all sewn up and then you can go back to the ward. Your husband's waiting for you, isn't he?'

She sniffed and nodded. 'He's left the other one with my mum—can I have a photo of the babe?'

'Of course—I think one's probably been taken, hasn't it?'

The damp nurse nodded. 'Yes, it's here—it'll be ready in a second. There—it's a lovely one.'

While Mrs Partington clutched the Polaroid photo of her baby, Anne removed the placenta, watched until the bleeding had stopped and then closed up. They had used oxytocin this time, although it was no longer used routinely, because after the uterus had been distended so far it sometimes had difficulty clamping down again after delivery and so the placental site was more likely to haemorrhage.

Luck was with Anne, however, and she was able to complete the operation with a sense of satisfaction.

In fact Jake made her take over his entire list the following day, talking her through each of the operations.

'You're good,' he said as they finished up that evening. 'Are you going to stick to Obs and Gynae?'

'I think so—I don't know. That or paediatric surgery.'

He shook his head. 'Don't go for Paeds. You're much too tender-hearted, it would destroy you.'

She smiled. 'You're probably right.'

'Of course I'm right—I'm always right. Have you heard from Beth?'

'Mmm. I had a long chat to her on the phone last night. She's been shopping with Grannie and bankrupted her, by the sound of it!'

Jake frowned. 'Shopping for what?'

'Clothes—she'd grown again.'

'So buy her some—I'll pay for them.'

Anne felt her muscles clench. 'That isn't necessary. My mother enjoys shopping with her, and they can afford it easily.'

'So can I, and I don't want handouts from your parents.'

His jaw was hard, his mouth set in an uncompromising line. Anne sighed.

'Don't be difficult, Jake. I don't want handouts at all, but sometimes you just have to grin and bear it.'

She walked into the ladies' changing-room and he followed her to the door.

'Annie——'

'Later.' She shut the door in his face. She knew she was only stalling for time, but after the afternoon list she felt washed out and definitely unready for another round with Jake.

The circulating nurse smiled at her knowingly. 'Lover-boy giving you trouble? I'll take him off your hands if you like.'

'Help yourself,' she said flatly, and, stripping off her green theatre garb, she walked towards the shower.

'Water's cold,' the nurse said helpfully.

She turned back again.

'I'll shower at home.' She tugged on her clothes in stony silence, and ignored him in the corridor, all round the ward while they checked their post-op patients and back to the lift.

'Going home?' he asked as she stepped into the lift.

'Goodnight, Jacob.'

He stood there, grimly watching her as the gap narrowed and the doors hissed shut.

She couldn't believe she'd got away with it.

He would be furious when he finally caught up with her, but she wouldn't allow him to throw his weight around and order her to accept his charity. Damn it, the food shopping and the car were enough—more than enough.

She flicked on the immersion heater, flung some meat and vegetables into a casserole, then popped a note through his door telling him to come round at seven. She wasn't foolish enough to imagine she could stall him for long, so she might as well give him some of his food and then half the time his mouth would be tied up with eating.

Satisfied with her plan, she went upstairs and ran a bath, wallowing in the warm, scented water while unbidden images of Jake teased her mind and body.

Damn him, she thought. Since he's come back there's been no peace. All day long I have to work with him, and then all night he torments my sleep with crazy dreams.

Her body warmed with the memory of last night's dream, and she stood up and soaped herself roughly. She told herself it was quite natural for an adult woman to feel stirrings of desire for an attractive man, and it didn't mean she had to act on it, but she secretly hoped he wouldn't put her resolve to the test. It was unlikely that he would tonight, though. He was still ranting on the money kick.

Stepping out of the bath, she rubbed her hair roughly dry, scrubbed at her limbs and cursed the inadequate central heating.

A door banged in Jake's house, and seconds later she heard her name.

She opened the bathroom door meaning to call over the banisters to him, but he was there, right by her, his foot on the top step and his eyes suddenly filled with hunger.

She clutched the towel round her and stared back at him, her thoughts in turmoil.

'Sorry—I didn't realise—I'll go—oh, God, Annie. . .'

He stepped forward and took the towel from her nerveless fingers.

'No!' she whispered, but he either didn't hear or didn't listen, because he closed the gap between them and lifted her into his arms.

His heart was pounding under her ear, its rhythm in time with her own as he kicked the bedroom door shut behind him and lowered her carefully to the bed.

His own clothes despatched with swift economy of movement, he was beside her before she could gather her wits.

She meant to protest, but his name came out like a plea, and seconds later she was kissing him back, glorying in the feel of his strong, sleek-muscled body beneath her eager hands.

It had been so long—so very, very long, and she felt her body contract with apprehension as he moved over her.

'Annie?' he murmured, suddenly hesitant.

'It's OK—it's just—I haven't. . . Since Beth I haven't. . .'

'I won't hurt you,' he whispered. His touch gentled, soothing now, then slowly building again until she writhed beneath him, his claiming of her so subtly controlled that she was almost unaware of it.

She breathed his name, her lips against his skin, and he cradled her tenderly as he began to move.

'Oh. . .!' Her soft sigh of surprise drew a chuckle from him, but then his face sobered and his eyes burned with flame.

'I love you, Annie,' he said raggedly, and then, dropping his face into her shoulder, he matched his rhythm to hers, driving her higher and higher until she was sure she would die, then holding her through the wild explosion and the gentle drift back to earth.

CHAPTER EIGHT

As ANNIE'S heart slowed, so her common sense returned, like a bucketful of cold water.

Jake eased his weight off her and settled on to his back with a sigh, one hand possessively on her hip.

'Wow,' he said softly, almost reverently.

'This doesn't change anything, Jake,' she told him, her voice flat and emotionless.

It took a second for her words to sink in, then he raised himself on one elbow and turned to face her. 'What do you mean, it doesn't change anything? Damn it, Annie—hell, you mean it, don't you?' He scanned her face, then dropped back against the pillows, his eyes shocked. 'My God, you really mean it.'

'Jake, it was just——'

'Don't! Don't say it, Annie. If you tell me that was just sex—hell, just don't say it.'

'Why not? It's true, and just sex was good enough for you before——'

'I never said that was just sex——'

'Just that it needn't make any difference. And that's the point I'm making now. Whatever happened just now, for whatever reason, nothing's changed—including me.'

She slid her legs over the bed and started to dress, suddenly conscious of her nakedness.

'Your body's still just as beautiful as ever.'

'Hardly,' she snorted.

He knelt on the bed and removed the sweatshirt she was about to put on from her hands.

'Your breasts are fuller.'

'They also sag, and I've got stretch marks. So what?'

'Exactly. You're still beautiful. Don't be ashamed.'

'I'm not ashamed,' she told him firmly, tugging the sweatshirt. 'I'm cold.'

'You don't look it,' he said, eyeing her blush with interest.

'Well, I am,' she snapped. 'Now give me back that sweatshirt.'

'Say please.'

'Jake. . .'

He grinned and handed it back, and as she turned and tugged it over her head she could feel his eyes on her back, sliding over every curve and hollow like a hot caress.

When she turned he was standing beside her, gloriously naked, unashamedly aroused.

She swallowed, grabbed the rest of her clothes and fled back into the bathroom.

How could she have been so *stupid*? What on earth had possessed her that she had allowed him to carry her off like that to bed and—and——?

'Oh, damn!'

She sank on to the edge of the bath and let the tears fall.

'Annie?' The doorknob rattled gently. 'Darling, are you OK?'

'Go away,' she mumbled.

'What about the casserole?'

'Take it with you—I don't care. How can you think about your stomach?'

The door opened. 'I was thinking about yours—you're thinner than you should be.'

She glared at him. 'I didn't ask you to look at my

body, so don't come in here now and have the gall to criticise it!'

'I wasn't——'

'You were! Now get out.'

'Annie, I——'

'Get out!'

The door closed softly, and she listened with cold dread as his footsteps faded down the hall. The sound of the front door shutting behind him was one of the loneliest things she had ever heard.

The phone rang at seven the following morning.

'Annie? It's Jo—what's this about Maggie?'

'Oh—you're back.'

'Yes, we're back. We got back late last night. Well?'

Anne was still too stunned with sleep and the amazing stupidity of her actions the night before to cope with Jo. 'Can I ring you when I've had time to wake up?'

Jo's voice was immediately contrite. 'Sorry—I was consumed with curiosity——'

'So why not ring Maggie?'

'She's on call—I couldn't get hold of her. I tell you what, why don't I come for breakfast?'

'No,' Anne said firmly. 'I've got a bone to pick with you, and when I pick it I want plenty of time. I'll ring you tonight.'

'Come for a meal tomorrow after the wedding—I'll cook an Indian.'

'Are you sure he won't mind?' Anne asked drily, wound up the conversation and hung up.

She plucked up her courage to go to work, but Jake was in a clinic all morning and operating all afternoon, so she managed to avoid him.

Only two more days, she told herself, and then he would be gone.

He was on call over the weekend, so his house was quiet that night. Anne was shocked at how much she missed hearing him moving around. It was going to be awful when he left—and Beth would miss him dreadfully.

She wondered where he would go and what he would do, and told herself she was only interested because he would need to keep in touch with Beth.

Saturday morning dawned clear and bright, but cold. She did the washing and hung it out, cleaned the house from top to bottom to take her mind off Jake, and then, not spoilt for choice, she put on the outfit she had bought for Jo's and Alex's wedding in December and made her way to the hospital.

The wedding was in the chapel, and she arrived in time to meet up with Jo and Alex near the door.

Alex had his left arm in a sling.

'What did you do?' she hissed.

Jo grinned. 'He fell off a bar stool. I'll tell you about it later.'

'I was stone-cold sober,' Alex muttered in her ear.

'You should have been drunk—you would have made a better job of landing,' Anne told him with a strained smile.

Jo shot her a worried look.

'Are you OK?'

'No thanks to you. I'll talk to you later—at length!' Anne promised darkly.

They took their seats, and Jo looked down the aisle to where the groom was sitting with his best man.

'The ship's rat is looking very dashing,' she whispered.

'Behave,' Anne told her. 'You got me in trouble with that expression.'

Just then the organist launched into the traditional bridal march and they swivelled round to see Maggie appear at the top of the aisle, her face radiant, her long red-gold hair cascading down her back under her veil. Her dress was a soft not-quite-white, perfect with her creamy skin, and around her neck lay a string of perfect pearls.

'What a lovely dress!' Jo murmured. 'And aren't the pearls fabulous? Doesn't she look beautiful?'

Anne felt a lump form in her throat.

She could be doing that, too, if only she could trust Jake. . .

'Anything I can do to help?'

'You could lay the table—here are the things.'

Jo pushed a pile of cutlery over the worktop towards her. 'We'll eat in here, it's cosier.'

Anne scooped up the cutlery and took it over to the table in the corner of the big kitchen-breakfast-room.

'Four?' she said, eyeing the cutlery with a feeling of foreboding.

'Yes—Jake's coming. I'm dying to see him, it's been so long. Wasn't it a lovely wedding? I thought Maggie looked absolutely radiant.'

'Jo——'

'Pass me the salt and pepper, would you, Annie?' She lifted her face to Alex's. 'Hello, darling. Manage to change OK?'

'For goodness' sake, I've only sprained my wrist. Anne, can I get you a drink?'

She let out her breath on a sigh. 'I think you'd better—something strong. Strychnine, or whatever.'

He handed her a glass of red wine. 'Try that— it's an Australian Cabernet.'

She sipped the smooth wine appreciatively. 'Much nicer than strychnine—thank you!'

He chuckled. 'So, how's it been without us? Is that why you're ready to poison yourself?'

'Not at all. Actually, you're both completely dispensable.'

'I'm relieved to hear it, because I'm going to be out of action for quite a while with this wrist. Thank God Jake's around and doesn't have any other commitments!'

'Jake?' Anne said incredulously, and then sagged back against her chair. 'Oh, no, please!'

Jo eyed her warily. 'No? Really? What happened?'

Anne sighed. 'Look there's something you ought to know——'

'I'll get it.'

As the chimes of the doorbell faded, Alex strode down the hall and opened the door to Jake.

'What ought we to know?' Jo asked.

Anne took a deep breath. 'Beth is Jake's daughter.'

The wooden spoon landed on the floor with a splat.

'*What*?'

'I felt a bit like that,' Jake said, walking into the room. 'I have to thank you for putting me in touch with her, however inadvertently.' He kissed her on the cheek, picked up the wooden spoon and dropped it in the sink.

'Oh, God, what have I done?' Jo wailed, looking from Anne to Jake and back again in despair.

'Nothing that shouldn't have been done long ago,' Anne said quietly.

'But—why didn't you tell us? Why didn't you tell Jake?'

'Because I'm a feckless, footloose, itinerant playboy, that's why.'

'Rubbish.'

Jake shrugged. 'That's what I told her. Perhaps you'll have more success. Hello, Annikins.'

'Don't,' she gritted. 'Jo, if you'll excuse me I'll go home——'

'Nonsense,' Jake said, and, putting his hand on her shoulder, he pushed her firmly back into her seat. 'Sit down and stop running away from everything. I'm on call so I'm quite likely to have to go myself shortly. You might as well stay, then you can tell these good people what a perfect bastard I've been. Perhaps you'd like to start with the car.'

'Car?' Alex and Jo said in unison.

Anne glared at him. 'You tell them—it was your idea.'

'OK.' He dropped into a chair, stretched out his legs and locked his hands behind his head. 'Anne bought a car—a real wreck. I didn't want my daughter travelling in something so patently unsafe, so I bought her another one.'

Jo craned her neck over the sink and peered through the window. 'So you did—my God, and she accepted it!'

Jake snorted and Anne sighed heavily.

'On loan,' she added.

'Ah!' Jo said thoughtfully, and walked over to the table, putting down a bowl of peanuts and looking from one to the other. 'Well, forgive me for being so thick, but just when did Beth—I mean, how——? I didn't know you two—oh, help me! Say something!'

'Finals night.'

Jo sat down with a plonk next to Jake and gazed at him. Her pale green-blue eyes were alive with curiosity.

'Finals night?'

Jake noded slowly.

'Oh, my God.' Her eyes swivelled to Anne. 'I thought you were very upset the next morning, but I never dreamed—oh, Jake! So what do you think of her? Isn't she a gem?'

'Amazing.' His voice was slightly choked. 'She's the most wonderful thing that's ever happened to me—with the exception of her mother.'

'Oh, Jake, leave it out,' Annie said in despair.

'So when are you getting married?' Jo asked.

Jake closed his eyes, but not before everyone round the table had seen the flash of pain in them. 'Apparently we're not.'

'Annie?'

'Could we please drop the subject?'

Jo stared at her for a long while, then her shoulders lifted and fell in a long, troubled sigh and she stood up. 'Sure. Tell us about work. Who's had babies, who hasn't—how's Lizzi Hamilton getting on?'

'Fine—now. She had a little girl.'

Jo spun round. 'She what? When? Oh, my goodness, was she all right? Tell me!'

'She was fine in the end,' Jake said. 'Bit of a struggle, but she managed. Ross was the one who couldn't cope.'

'You didn't do a section?' Alex asked quietly.

'No need. That's one thing I learnt in Romania—if you don't have anaesthetics available, you very quickly learn what you can and can't get away with. She wasn't at risk—not like some of those poor women. God, it was awful.'

'Tell me all about it,' Jo said. 'The good, the bad and the ugly.'

Jake laughed humourlessly. 'It's all ugly, Jo. Well, nearly all. The relief workers are doing what they can, but the Romanians have lived for so long in a brutalised and dehumanised society that sometimes I think they've forgotten how to care any more. Even if they did, what can they do about it? The facilities are worse than non-existent, the midwives are inadequately trained, the hygiene is a joke—it's disgusting. Appalling. The first week I was there if I wasn't on the point of being sick with the awful smell, I was in tears. Then I just pulled up my sleeves and got on with it. At one point I was doing nearly forty terminations a day—they did over two hundred a day in our hospital alone at that time, but it's getting better now, thank God. You imagine doing an abortion without an anaesthetic—all you can offer is comfort and the knowledge that she won't have to bring yet another disadvantaged child into a cruel and bitter world.'

Alex nodded. 'I had a friend who went for a while. He was really very distressed by the whole thing.'

Jake smiled grimly. 'I can imagine. It is pretty distressing, but it isn't all bad. While I was there I went up into Moldavia and met a woman called Barbara who's revamped an orphanage in Goesti. They've got just under forty children there living as a family, and gradually they're getting a response from the children. It's a new concept, actually, in that because of the commitment of the volunteers they're able to let the children stay until they're seven. Usually they're moved on at three, after they've been "assessed" on things like potty training, walking, speech and so on. If they fail the "test" they're classed as irrecuperables, and the homes for the irrecuperables are unbelievably squalid.'

'But why are there so many "irrecuperables"?' Jo asked indignantly. 'Even in the worst Third World countries the children walk and talk. Surely to God not that many can be injured at birth?'

Jake's face settled into weary resignation. 'They don't have to be injured. The health care has been so bad that the children are disadvantaged from before conception. When they're born, they're often ill, and then they go into the hospitals. Mothers aren't allowed to visit, so the children are distressed and won't eat. There's no formula milk, so they're given gruel that they can't tolerate, so they deteriorate. They get infections, they get more ill, then the parents can't have them back because the children are too ill to cope with, so they then get moved to the "orphanages". Most of the children aren't orphans at all, but simply abandoned because their parents don't know what else to do.'

Anne felt almost physically sick at the thought of all that human suffering. 'What happens then?' she asked quietly.

'As I said, when they get to three, they're assessed, but if they've never been out of their cots and their limbs are deformed because they've been tied in and nobody's ever tried to talk to them then of course they can't walk and talk, and none of them are potty trained. At Goesti they're giving them formula milk, getting the children up on their feet, talking to them, teaching them in the schoolroom, so many that might be classed as irrecuperables now won't be by the time they're seven, and so they should be able to live a more normal life. The difference Barbara's charity and countless other little charities like it are making is very profound, but it only lasts as long as the volunteers are prepared to stay. Some of the children will still be irrecuperables—the ones who'll never get to school, who ultimately end up in adult mental homes. Some will die because they have HIV, because Ceauçescu in his infinite wisdom decided that buying cheap African blood and transfusing the newborns was more cost-effective than giving them milk.' He gave a harsh laugh. 'Have you ever seen a baby with full-blown AIDS?'

Jo swallowed and Alex reached over the table, gripping her hand.

'Amy,' Alex said quietly, his voice not quite steady, 'the baby we hope to adopt, is the daughter of a drug addict who was HIV positive. We won't know for more than a year if she's been infected *in utero*.'

Jake's face paled, and he reached out and covered both their hands, squeezing tight.

'I'm sorry,' he said in a choked whisper. 'Oh, God, I'm so sorry.'

Jo shrugged and smiled bravely. 'It may not even be our problem, of course.' She sniffed, blotted her eyes on Alex's proffered handkerchief and stood up. 'Why don't we eat?' she asked brightly.

Anne was still trying to come to terms with the fact that Jake, far from swanning around in New York earning an indecent amount of money, had actually been working in sub-human conditions.

'Did you get sponsorship?'

He shook his head. 'No, I used what I'd managed to save before I left the New York clinic and supplemented it with locum work. It was pretty tight sometimes.'

'Oh, yes—which is why you're running around in a BMW and managed to buy me a car——'

'I've had the BMW since I got back to England, before I decided to go to Romania—and I took out a loan to buy your car.'

'A loan?' She was stunned. He was always saying he didn't have much money, but she just assumed he meant—well, to be truthful, she hadn't really believed him. But if he'd got through his savings and been doing locum work. . .

'When did you go?' she asked.

'About eighteen months ago, the first time. I've been back several times since for a month or two at a time, in between doing my FRCS and locum in London to subsidise myself. Believe me, I was ready to leave when Jo contacted me. You can only do so much before your heart breaks.'

Anne was astounded. 'You mean you've been in London some of that time? You never said anything.'

'You never asked.'

'But—Jo, why didn't you tell me?'

Jo looked at Anne with eyes heavy with silent reproach. 'Oh, I tried. Whenever I mentioned him, you changed the subject. I always felt there was something more than indifference in your attitude, but I never in my wildest dreams imagined it could be Beth. I thought. . . I don't know, perhaps I thought secretly you were in love with him—that's why I pushed you together now.'

Jake snorted. 'No such luck, Jo-Jo. She hates my guts.'

Anne met the gentle reproof in his eyes with rising misery.

'I don't hate your guts, Jake. You know that.'

'Do I? I don't think I know anything any more—except that you didn't care enough to contact me in nearly eight years.'

Anne lowered her eyes. How could she have contacted him? He would have wanted to know about Beth, and she couldn't have told him much before he'd asked for a photo, and that would have been it. And anyway, she had been trying hard to forget him and build a life for them both. That had been difficult enough without adding his curiosity to the equation.

'You know why I didn't contact you,' she reminded him quietly.

'Oh, yes, of course. . . I'm a footloose, itinerant—how does it go?'

She glared at him. 'Stop it or I'll leave.'

He stood up. 'Forget it—I suddenly lost my appetite. Sorry, Jo. Maybe another night.' He bent down and kissed her cheek, then let himself quietly out of the front door.

Anne propped her elbows on the table and stared morosely into her red wine.

'Go on, then. Tell me I'm being unreasonable.'

Alex stood up and walked over to the kitchen area and helped himself to a loaded plate of rice and vegetable curry.

'I think I'll leave you two girls to sort this out in private,' he told them, and closed the door behind him.

Jo went over to the cooker and dished up two plates of curry. 'So, do you think you're being unreasonable?' she asked, plonking the plates down on the table.

Anne sighed. 'I don't know any more. I didn't think so, but sometimes I wonder—but you know what he was like, Jo.'

Jo speared a succulent piece of cauliflower and waved it in the air. 'I know what he was like, but do you? Sometimes I don't think you ever really knew him.'

'Oh, come on, he was an alley-cat!'

'Was he?' She speared a carrot. 'Or was he just a gregarious young man, hiding his real feelings by partying?'

Anne poked at her plate. 'What real feelings?'

Jo laid down her fork. 'He's loved you for years, you

know. All the time you were with Duncan, he waited quietly in the wings to see which way it would go; in fact, for a time I thought you'd get together because you saw so much of each other and you were so damn good together—and then you came back after that last summer and announced that you were engaged to Duncan, and I think it nearly broke his heart.'

Anne was appalled. 'But—he never said anything to me.'

'He didn't like to, because of Duncan. He was always very fair like that. He hated unfaithfulness. That's why I'm surprised he slept with you on finals night.'

'He didn't plan to, I don't think. He came back and found me in his room, crying my eyes out into his pillow. It just sort of—happened, after that.'

'If you'd known how he felt—would it have made any difference?'

Anne shrugged. 'Maybe. I doubt it. I think once he'd got me where he thought he wanted me he would have got bored. Look how quickly he got through his girlfriends.'

'Or appeared to.' Jo topped up Anne's wine. 'Did you never think it might all be a front?'

'Don't be daft! They all talked about him—he was a great catch.'

'And how many of them would have admitted that he wouldn't sleep with them and had dumped them because they bored him?'

'He didn't, though.'

'He did, though—very often. You forget, he used to tell me all his woes, especially where you were concerned.' She fiddled with her curry. 'Why didn't you reply to his letters?'

'Letters?' Anne eyed her friend curiously. 'What letters?'

'That first year—the year you were pregnant. He wrote twice, I think. He was very hurt that you didn't reply.'

Anne shook her head. 'I never got them—he must have forgotten to post them. You remember the time our electricity was cut off, and he found the letter in his jacket when it went to the cleaners'?'

Jo smiled. 'Maybe. He still loves you, Annie.'

Anne put her fork down and pushed her almost untouched meal away. 'No, he just thinks he does. It's seeing me again, and finding out about Beth.'

'Is that why he sent you his love with every letter that he ever wrote me for the past eight years?'

Anne met Jo's gentle eyes. She was stunned. 'Every letter?'

'Every one. He's never forgotten you.'

She remembered his words right back at the beginning of the previous week, when she had told him not to forget their arrangement for the evening. 'When have I ever forgotten you?' he had said.

She remembered other things he had said, things about medicine and the hospital and terminations. His comments about birth control had obviously related to Romania—and his comments about the miracles of modern technology not being available to everyone, likewise. She had thought he was criticising the British health care system, but in fact he was trying to talk to her.

Had she listened, asked, taken any interest in the course of his life over the past seven or eight years?

No. She'd been totally preoccupied with making him understand her life with Beth, and holding him at a distance, terrified of letting him into their lives in case his love disturbed the even tenor of their monotonous existence. She'd rebuffed every little kindness and had made snap judgements about him based on the little information Jo had managed to get past her barrier of apparent indifference.

If Jo was right, then he was a very different person from the one whose memory she had carried all these years—and if he was so different, was it not possible that she was in love with a mirage and not the real man at all?

And although he said he loved her, did he really, or did he love the girl she had once been?

And there was still the problem of her fictitious engagement to Duncan to explain to him.

She stood up.

'I need to go home and think, Jo. There's so much to absorb. I don't really know if it will make any difference, but I owe it to Beth to understand her father better than I apparently do. Even if we don't get together, we've still got to communicate over the next few years.'

Jo stood up and hugged Anne. 'Don't torture yourself. It will all come right. I'm only too sorry that I put you both in that position, but I had no idea—I can't believe I was so stupid, because of course they are incredibly alike. How did they take to each other?'

Anne smiled wistfully. 'They both fell head over heels in love. She's totally besotted with him, and given a chance he'd spoil her rotten.'

'Annie?' Jo stopped her with a hand on her arm. 'Give him that chance—if you feel you can. He won't let you down. You could do worse than to marry him.'

'He's tried marriage before, of course. What about that? That was hardly a resounding success.'

Jo shook her head. 'You'll have to ask him about his marriage. He told me very little, but I'm sure he'll tell you all you want to know.'

'Were they ever happy?'

Jo shook her head. 'I don't think so, not really.'

'Then why on earth did he marry her?'

'I don't know. You'll have to ask him that.' Jo opened the front door and looked out. 'Nice car.'

Anne smiled wanly. 'Yes—yes, it is, isn't it? I'm sorry we ruined your evening.'

Jo hugged her again. 'Don't worry about it. Give yourselves time—it's been years since you've had any time together. Give him a chance to prove himself to you—for your own sake, as much as Beth's.'

She thought about Jo's words all the following day while she waited for her parents to return Beth, and when she saw Jake on Monday morning she was determined to find time to talk to him.

However, it wasn't as easy as it might have been. Having been on call, he was very tired and uncommunicative, and Anne felt she needed his full attention before she said anything.

She wasn't sure, anyway, what she did want to say to him, and by Monday evening he had her scuttling for cover again.

'When are you going to tell Beth about me?' he asked as they left for home together.

She shrugged. 'I don't know. You were on duty yesterday. I though perhaps the weekend, when we've got time together.'

He shook his head. 'No. Tonight, Annie. I won't wait.'

She looked at him, taking in the grey tinge to his skin, the dark shadows under his eyes, the way it seemed too much effort to hold his body straight.

'All right, tomorrow, then, but tonight you're both too tired to cope with it.'

To her surprise he agreed, and she spent the whole night and all of the following day mentally chewing her nails down to the elbow over the scene to come.

In fact it was easy.

Beth was trying on some of her new clothes when Jake arrived early on Tuesday evening, and she showed him her new sweatshirt.

'Look,' she said, and dragged him to the mirror in the hall. 'Your jumper's the same colour as mine—see.'

They stood in front of the mirror, Jake behind her, hands on her shoulders, and looked at each other.

'You even look like me,' she said in delight. 'You're hair's nearly black, like mine, and you've got brown eyes like me.'

'Yes,' Jake said gently. 'We do look very alike.'

Anne stood beside them. 'You look a bit like me, too.'

Beth eyed all their reflections doubtfully. 'I look more like Jake.'

Anne drew a deep breath, met Jake's eyes in the mirror and looked back to Beth. 'Children often look like their parents.'

She twisted round and looked at them. 'So if you and Jake got married, people would think he was my daddy?'

'Would you like that?' Jake asked. 'If people thought I was your daddy?'

Beth's brows quirked together in a little frown. 'I'd like it better if you really were. Otherwise you'd be my stepfather, and I'd rather have a real daddy. I don't think I want a stepfather but I wouldn't mind if it was you.'

Jake's jaw clenched. 'I wouldn't be your stepfather, Beth.'

The child frowned doubtfully. 'Why not?'

Anne crouched down and took Beth's hand. 'Because Jake is your daddy—your real daddy.'

Her eyes widened like saucers, and she looked from one to the other in disbelief before throwing herself into Jake's arms and bursting into tears.

'I wanted a daddy so much,' she sobbed, and for a moment Anne thought he would crush Beth as he cradled her against his chest. Then his arms gentled and he sat down on the hall floor and lifted her into his lap, rocking her back and forth while the tears streamed down his cheeks.

'I love you, Jake,' Beth whispered.

'Oh, Beth——' His voice cracked and he buried his head in her hair.

Anne couldn't take any more. There was a dull, heavy pain over her heart—a pain that felt almost like grief. She told herself that she wasn't losing Beth, but in a way she was, because she was losing her monopoly of her daughter and would be forced to make decisions about who had her for birthdays and Christmases and so on.

She sat at the kitchen table and tried very hard not to be selfish, to be glad for Jake and Beth that they had each other now and were both so thrilled with the discovery, but a little part of her cried, What about me? I want to be part of it, too!

She sniffed hard. Jake had asked her, and she knew full well she had her daughter's approval, but she couldn't take the risk. What if he got bored with being a parent and left them? Or just simply took a mistress—which was more likely, as otherwise he would lose his daily contact with Beth. Anne had no faith in her ability to hold him.

Oh, it was obvious from talking to Jo that Jake had

imagined himself in love with her, but would the reality be quite different?

How would Beth cope with being let down by him? Had they done the right thing to tell her?

There were murmurings from the hall now, Beth's little voice alternating with Jake's deep rumble. Any minute now the questions would start, and she would have to shatter her daughter's dreams.

Unless she married him.

Standing up, she blew her nose and splashed her face with cold water, and then went out into the hall.

Jake and Beth were still sitting on the floor in a tangle of arms and legs, and their faces were both alight with happiness.

Jake reached out a hand and pulled her down to them, wrapping her hard against his side.

'OK?' he asked softly. His voice was still a little gruff.

Anne nodded. 'How about you?'

'Oh, I'm fine—never better.'

Beth wriggled across his lap into Anne's arms, and linked an arm around each of their necks, pulling their heads together. Then she gave a big sigh of satisfaction.

'Happy, Tuppence?'

'Mmm. Hungry.'

Jake chuckled, his chest shaking against Anne's shoulder.

'Why don't we go out to eat?'

'Pizza Hut?' Beth asked, bobbing her head up.

Twenty minutes later they were taking their seats and a waitress came to take their order.

'My daddy likes pizza,' Beth confided in the waitress.

The girl smiled. 'Good. We like satisfied customers.'

'I expect they'll get married soon,' Beth added. 'Like one of those soppy films on the telly. Romance and all that stuff. They kiss when I'm not supposed to be looking.'

Jake covered his face with his hand and made a choked sound. Anne smiled at the astonished waitress, finished ordering and sent her on her way.

'What's wrong with Jake?' Beth asked innocently.

'Nothing. I expect he's getting a cold.'

'You will, though, won't you?'

'What, get a cold?'

'No—get married!'

There was a strained silence. Jake looked up and met Anne's anguished expression, his eyes gently questioning.

'Well?' he asked softly.

She swallowed and took a deep breath.

'Yes, we'll get married.'

'Oh, yippee!' Beth shrieked, and bounced up and down on her chair.

Anne met Jake's eyes and watched them fill with promises, and wondered why she felt as if she'd just thrown herself off a cliff.

CHAPTER NINE

'YOU won't regret it, I promise you,' Jake told her later, after their daughter was finally in bed asleep.

'I hope not. I'm only doing it for Beth.'

'I know that.' He looked away, then looked back, his expression strangely intent. 'Whatever your motivation, I hope you aren't harbouring any illusions about this marriage; I mean, if we get married, we do it for real—and for keeps.'

She met the blaze in his eyes for a second and looked away, suddenly shy. 'I know. Don't worry, I'll co-operate. You won't have to go without your conjugal rights.'

He laughed a little wryly. 'I wasn't thinking of your co-operation so much as your participation.'

'Yes, well,' she said with a touch of irony, 'you seem to have a way of getting that, too.' She glanced at the calendar on the kitchen wall. 'I suppose it will have to be Easter. I'm off from Good Friday for two weeks.'

'OK. That's—what? About five and a half weeks? Does that give you long enough?'

She shot him an astonished look. 'For what? We aren't having an elaborate wedding—I thought the register office——'

'Not church?'

'Well—you're divorced.'

He shrugged. 'The chaplain might still do it—I'll have a word with him. I met his son in Romania.'

'The old pals' act,' she said drily, and shook her head

in despair at his cocky grin. 'Whatever, Jake, I don't think we want a big fussy wedding.'

'Pity. I think Beth would make rather a lovely bridesmaid. Anyway, we'll talk about it tomorrow. You look tired. Goodnight—and Annie?'

She met his eyes.

'I don't know if you have any idea what you've given me, but thank you.'

He brushed a chaste kiss on her cheek and let himself out.

She watched him go with a leaden heart. Oh, she knew, all right. She'd given him his daughter—but at what cost?

She went upstairs and stood in Beth's room, watching her daughter by the dim glow from the nightlight, and prayed that she hadn't just made the second biggest mistake of her life.

Her plans for a quiet wedding were dismissed before they were even verbalised.

'It's going to be a fabulous wedding!' Jo said emphatically. 'Goodness knows we've had to wait long enough.'

'Perhaps you'll let my grandmother organise it,' Maggie suggested. 'After all, she was thwarted over mine.'

As they both still had stars in their eyes following their own weddings, it was pointless trying to get them on her side.

'Will I be able to be a bridesmaid?' Beth wanted to know. She obviously wasn't going to be an ally either!

'I've spoken to the chaplain and explained the circumstances, and he'd be delighted to marry us in the chapel,' Jake told her the following afternoon.

Anne gave up. In the face of her doubts, the manner

of execution seemed of minor importance compared to the end result.

Fortunately they were kept busy.

Jo was back at work, of course, and Alex wandered in and out, frustrated by his enforced inactivity. There was no way he could operate until his wrist settled, and so he haunted clinics and delivery-rooms and Theatre, scowling at Jo whenever she told him to get out of her way and stop worry-gutting.

'If you want to do something useful,' she told him at the end of the first week, 'you can go and hassle Social Services and see if you can't get some news on Amy.'

Amy was an orphaned baby whom they hoped to adopt, but the adoption agencies were taking what seemed like forever to give Jo and Alex a decision. First they had to clear the hurdle of being passed as suitable parents, and some of the interviews had been quite gruelling.

In the meantime the baby was fostered by a very caring woman who was quite happy for Jo to visit Amy as often as she wanted. But the wait was tearing Jo apart—that and the possibility that Amy might be HIV positive and that they might lose her anyway. They wouldn't know the answer to that question until she was about eighteen months, by which time, as Jo pointed out, she might well be officially someone else's daughter.

'Will you go on working if you get her?' Anne asked over coffee one day.

'Oh, no! I'll hand over to Jake. He and Alex seem to be getting on well, and you work well with him.'

It was a possibility Anne hadn't even considered, but as she spent more and more time with him in Theatre and the delivery-room, she had to agree. Although personally she might have her doubts about him, professionally she had to admit that he was an excellent surgeon and his warmly generous manner had all the patients eating out of his hand.

'I hope he delivers me,' Bron Henderson said one day in Antenatal. 'He's so easy to talk to. I like Alex, but Jake is somehow so friendly. It's as if he really cares about how it goes, and he was brilliant with Lizzi Hamilton.'

'Oh, I'm sure Alex cares,' Anne defended, but secretly she agreed. Alex was very self-contained and conservative, whereas Jake was likely to sit on the bed and finish off the crossword, or read all the cards on the bedside locker. Both were excellent doctors, but Alex was only just starting to unbend under Jo's influence. Perhaps with time he would mellow, but never to the same extent as Jake, who had constantly had his wrist slapped during his training for being over-familiar with the patients.

In the event Bron got her wish the following week, because Jo and Alex had a meeting with the Social Services about Amy and Jake was covering.

Anne came on to the ward during the morning after doing a gynae round, and detected an air of excitement.

'What's ado?' she asked the midwives at the nurses' station.

'Dr Henderson's in the birthing-room. We're just waiting for news.'

Bron was a popular member of the hospital staff, and her husband Oliver was a highly respected consultant general surgeon. There was bound to be a great deal of interest.

Anne slipped through the door and found Jake, Bron and Oliver Henderson all kneeling on the floor. Bron was on a mattress, and there was the soothing aroma of oil of lavender in the air.

Jake looked up and smiled at her. 'Hi, there. Come to join the party?'

'Just wondered how it was going.'

Bron glanced up and smiled, too. 'Hello, Annie. Nearly there now, you're just in time for the best bit.'

As Anne watched, a look of intense concentration come over the young woman's face, and she gripped her husband's arm and made a deep, guttural sound low in the throat.

'Steady now,' the midwife warned, 'pant, Bron, pant!'

Seconds later they were laying Bron down and handing her a squalling, slippery little baby boy.

Oliver reached out a trembling finger and touched his son's hand tentatively. Immediately the tiny fingers wrapped around in a sure, strong grip.

'My God,' Oliver said incredulously, and hugged Bron, half laughing, half crying with joy. 'Oh, my God! Oh, wow! Would you look at that! Oh, Bron!'

Half an hour later he was still talking in exclamation marks.

By visiting time in the afternoon he had calmed down slightly, but he was still definitely on cloud nine.

Anne and Jake were just leaving the ward to go down to Gynae when he stuck his head out of the door of Bron's room.

'Thanks for this morning,' he said.

Jake shrugged. 'You're welcome. How are they both?'

'Fine—fantastic. I'm taking them home in the morning. Ross is going to cover for me for the next couple of days—well, he owes me a favour. I did it for him not so long ago.'

Anne smiled. 'There must be something in the water up on Surgical, I think.'

He chuckled. 'Maybe. Anyway, I just wanted to say thanks. I'm sorry I was so——' He waved his arms helplessly. 'It was just so incredible. I missed Livvy's birth by about eighteen months, and—well, today was very important to me.' He shrugged and laughed self-consciously. 'That probably doesn't make any sense to you.'

Jake laid a hand on his shoulder. 'It makes perfect sense,' he said with a quiet smile. 'I missed my daughter's birth by seven years. I know exactly what you're talking about.'

A golden-haired little cherub slipped between them and smiled up at them all. 'I've got a baby brother,' she announced.

Jake squatted down and grinned at her. 'I know. Is he being good?'

She puckered her little nose. 'He screams a bit.'

Oliver bent down and swung her up into his arms. 'I expect you did, too.' He looked back to Jake. 'Thanks for this morning, anyway. You made it all so simple and beautiful.'

Jake grinned. 'Bron did that all by herself. Sometimes it's like that.'

It wasn't always, however. Later that same week a woman was admitted following a car accident; Anne was on duty and Jake was on call, fortunately still in the hospital.

They met in A and E, where Ben Bradshaw, Maggie's new husband, was treating the woman in the resus. room.

'Nasty one, I'm afraid,' he told them as they went in. 'Looks like an antepartum haemorrhage—her membranes have gone and she's bleeding like crazy. I've ordered a cross-match and twelve units, and we've run in some plasma expander to boost her, but I think she might have other internal injuries as well. She's also heavily concussed and could have a skull fracture, but now didn't seem the time to worry about X-rays.'

Jake swiftly assessed the woman's condition and called Theatre from the phone on the wall.

'Any idea how many weeks she is?' Anne asked.

Ben shrugged. 'Husband's outside—he's been drinking so I don't know what you'll get out of him.'

'Doesn't matter,' Jake said. 'I think it might well be academic. Has he signed the consent forms?'

Ben nodded. 'Kathleen's dealing with that. Here she is—got the forms?'

'Here.' She handed them to Jake. 'Drunken bastard. The police are dealing with him now. If you ask me he should be taken out and strung up.'

The porter wheeled her up to Theatre while Jake and Annie scrubbed at twice the speed of light, and by the time they arrived in the operating-room she was on the table, anaesthetised and waiting.

Anne watched in horrified fascination as Jake made a long vertical incision and opened the abdomen at speed.

She held the clamps and retractors, tried to stay out of the way of the scrub nurse with the suction and kept all her spare fingers crossed. Surely they must be in time?

But they weren't. Although they had registered the baby's heartbeat at the start of the operation, by the time they reached the baby it was too late.

Jake was clinically efficient, sorted out the other internal injuries with Ross Hamilton's help and only later, in the little staffroom attached to the theatre, did Anne see so much as a flicker of emotion.

'What a damn waste,' he said, his voice tight and

heavy with fatigue. 'I thought I was finished with tragedies like that.'

Anne knew there was a great deal about Romania he would never be able to tell her; the anguish and the suffering, the waste of life, all ran too deep for words, but she wondered how he would be able to turn his back on it—and how she and Beth would cope without him if his conscience sent him back again.

She kept meaning to ask him about it, but somehow they were always too busy to stop, and in the evenings he seemed to be avoiding being alone with her. The first one back at the end of the day collected Beth and started supper, and then they would take it in turns to read with her after she had done her homework. Then, as soon as Beth was in bed, Jake would kiss Annie goodnight and leave.

Sometimes the kisses were chaste, sometimes gently passionate, but none ever challenged their self-control. Anne began to doubt even more her ability to hold him. One thing she was glad about—their one recent lapse in control hadn't resulted in a pregnancy, and she had subsequently gone to her GP and been put on the Pill. No way was she falling into that trap again!

In fact, her relief when she had discovered she wasn't pregnant was frightening; although she knew she hadn't enjoyed her labour, it was only the prospect of facing it again that had made her admit just how afraid she was.

Her parents' reaction to her forthcoming marriage was predictably mixed. Her mother was cautiously optimistic, and her father thought she was being highly irresponsible letting him back into her life.

Of the two, Anne secretly agreed more with her father. Although she defended her decision to the hilt, she was silently waiting for her suspicions to be proved right.

As the days passed and the wedding drew nearer, so her need to talk to Jake deepened. He took to going out again after he left her and Beth in the evenings, and she never asked where he went and he never told her, but her fear grew until in the end she was unable to voice it.

A week before the wedding, Jo collared her and Maggie and dragged them out to lunch. She refused to answer their questions, telling them they'd have to wait.

Finally they were seated in a little salad bar in the centre of town, their bowls and their curiosity overflowing.

'Well?' they asked, eyeing Jo suspiciously. 'What's it all about?'

'I'm celebrating!' she told them.

'Celebrating?'

She produced a letter from her bag with a flourish. '*Voilà*!'

Anne and Maggie grabbed it and scanned it rapidly.

'You've got Amy!' Maggie shrieked, and, totally ignoring all the turning heads, the three friends hugged each other, laughing and crying simultaneously.

When they were all seated again and the first incoherent moments had passed, Anne took her hand and squeezed it.

'That's fantastic news—does Alex know?'

'Oh, yes—he's out now, shopping for paint. He's going to do the nursery—we didn't dare until she was definitely ours, but now. . .well!'

They all laughed.

'Will he stop scowling at everyone?' Maggie asked.

Jo chuckled. 'Maybe. His wrist has been driving him

mad, but a least he's back at work now. That and not knowing about Amy haven't helped, and I don't think I've been very easy to live with.'

'You never were!' Anne said drily. 'The man has my unbounded admiration!'

Jo poked her tongue out. 'How can you? You were always so organised and fussy, you used to drive us mad! And as for Jake—I've never seen such a mess. How you two'll cope when you're married, God only knows.'

Anne's face immediately sobered. 'Yes, well, we'll both have to adapt a little, I imagine.'

Jo eyed her thoughtfully. 'Are you having second thoughts?'

Anne was silent for a long while, then lifted her chin. 'No—no second thoughts.'

She looked away from Jo's piercing scrutiny and fiddled very intently with her salad.

'I can't believe it's happening so soon—you don't seem to have talked about it at all,' Maggie said.

'Don't be silly—of course I've talked about it——'

'Well, only the arrangements for the reception at Jo's and Alex's house, but nothing else. Have you got your dress yet?'

'Dress?'

'Yes, you know—wedding dress? The thing you wear to get married in?'

'Don't be sarcastic, Maggie, I know what you're talking about.'

Maggie blinked. 'Sorry, it was meant to be a joke— Annie, are you sure everything's all right?'

'Of course I'm sure!' she said, rather more sharply than she had intended. 'As for the dress, I thought I'd wear the suit I had for Jo's wedding——'

'What?'

'No!'

They spoke together, exchanged a speaking look and then Jo called for the bill.

'We're going shopping,' she announced.

'Where?' Anne eyed her friends suspiciously.

'Come on.' They hustled her to her feet, steered her out of the restaurant and down the road, and turned into a little shopping arcade.

'Oh, no—look, I can't afford this sort of thing——'

'So bill you father. Come on.'

'He's already paying the caterers for the reception——'

'Oh, pooh! You aren't having to buy the car any more—come on, Annie, you're only going to do it once!'

The manageress of the bridal boutique recognised the three women instantly.

'Hello again, ladies!' she said with a warm smile of welcome. 'I didn't expect to see you again so soon— what can I do for you?'

Jo laughed. 'The bridesmaid's mother was so taken with the idea, she's trying it for herself. What can you find for her?'

'Really, I don't think——'

'Rubbish,' Jo put in. 'This is going to be a very special wedding, and it's going to need a very special dress.'

'Jo, I cannot stand there in the chapel in miles of frothy lace with my seven-year-old daughter just two feet behind me!'

The woman smiled understandingly. 'Perhaps not a conventional wedding dress, but something simple? A suit, perhaps?'

Anne sensed an ally. 'That would be fine—something sensible that I can wear again——'

'No!' Jo and Maggie chorused.

The manageress smiled and shrugged. 'Have a look at these—some of them, of course, could be worn again, but we find women seldom do. There's something almost sacred about the clothes you wear for such a special occasion, and often people like to hang them up and just look at them from time to time. How about this one?'

She held out a pale ivory silk *crêpe de Chine* suit, with a narrow skirt that ended on the knee and a semi-fitted short jacket with tiny rouleau buttons down the front.

'Wonderful!' Jo said instantly.

'Oh, I'm not sure——'

Jo took it from the manageress, glanced at the size tag and handed it to her. 'Go and try it on.'

'I'm being railroaded,' Anne said crossly.

'Yes. Try it.'

It was perfect, even she could see that. The only thing was, she looked—well, bridal was really the only word for it.

'Oh, so what? You are getting married, after all!' she told her reflection, and if there was a bit of her that wanted to try its damnedest to look good for Jake, so what?

'I'll take it,' she told the manageress.

Jo handed her a little pillbox hat and a pair of ivory stockings with a soft sheen. 'Underwear?'

Anne opened her mouth and shut it. Jo was obviously on a roll. 'Fine.' She added the silk and lace teddy to the rapidly growing pile.

'What about Beth?' Jo asked.

'Well—I thought the dress she wore to be your bridesmaid——'

'No!' her friends said in unison.

'Not for your wedding,' Jo added. 'It's very special for her.'

Anne sighed. 'I expect she's grown, anyway.'

Ten minutes later they left the shop, parcels in hand.

'There!' Jo said with satisfaction. 'Aren't you glad we dragged you out?'

Anne rolled her eyes. 'I need a coffee. . .come back to my house and we can try the dress on Beth—she's having lunch with a friend but I said I'd pick her up at three.'

Jo shook her head. 'I have to get back and help Alex with the nursery.'

'I don't,' Maggie said, 'and I could murder a coffee. Give me a lift, and Ben can come and pick me up later.'

Beth was, of course, delighted with her dress, and it fitted perfectly. Anne hung it in her wardrobe with her suit, and shut the door on them both.

There must have been something in her face, because Maggie gave her a funny look.

'Something wrong?' she asked quietly a few minutes later. Beth was playing outside with friends, and they were sitting in the kitchen overlooking the quiet cul-de-sac, keeping an eye on her.

Anne shook her head. 'I just hope that suit isn't too bridal. I really didn't mean to go for that sort of look.'

Maggie smiled. 'You'll look lovely—just the way a bride is supposed to look.'

Anne sighed. 'I just wish I felt the way a bride is supposed to feel!'

'There really is something wrong, isn't there?' Maggie said quietly.

Anne twiddled with the salt and pepper. 'Maybe I'm silly, but I just don't trust his motives. I wish I could be sure he wasn't marrying me to get to Beth.'

'Hmm,' Maggie murmured thoughtfully. 'You know what I think? I think he's using Beth to get you, not the other way round.'

Anne stared at her. 'Don't be daft, he's crazy about the child. He'd do anything for her.'

'But he's got her anyway. The courts would uphold his right to access and joint custody, and you've proved you're willing to be reasonable about it—that's not the problem. The problem is, the courts won't give him any access to you, and it's you he really wants.'

'I wish I could believe that,' Anne said sadly.

'Maybe you just have to trust him,' Maggie said. 'I didn't trust Ben. I nearly lost him because of it, and just because I kept jumping to conclusions. It all made perfect sense at the time, but things are seldom what they seem. Can't you talk to him?'

'What difference would it make? I have to marry him anyway for Beth's sake, and I dare say we'll be all right. We were always very good friends. Perhaps that'll be enough.'

But even their friendship seemed strained beyond endurance that last week before the wedding.

They were busy in the hospital with all the spring babies.

'It's all these impressionable young lovers who get carried away in the heat of the summer nights and forget to take precautions,' Sister said with a chuckle.

Neither Anne nor Jake laughed. It was just too close to home.

As she moved about her work more and more quietly, she was more than ever conscious of Jake's eyes on her, eyes that seemed to be filled with misgivings.

Was he having doubts, too?

Then on the Wednesday afternoon a woman was admitted with a twin pregnancy. Her labour was already quite well advanced although it had only started after lunch, and she explained cheerfully that her labours were all easy.

'In fact,' she said, 'I did ask Mr Carter if it would be all right for the children to be present for the birth—just at the end, you know.'

'What did he say?' Anne asked.

'That it would be up to the doctor attending me to decide if it would be suitable—I mean, obviously if I have to have forceps or anything it might be inadvisable, but otherwise. . .' She shrugged and smiled. 'We have prepared them, and they know what's happening.'

Anne wasn't sure. 'How old are they?' she asked doubtfully.

'Eight, five and three. They're with my mother now, she's picked them up from school and she's bringing them over now, just in case, but they'll want to be here to see the twins as soon as they're born, anyway.'

Anne chewed her lip. 'I don't think I can really make that sort of decision, Mrs Bailey. Can I ask Mr Carter?'

'Of course. Do you mind if I walk round for a bit?'

'No, please do. I'll be back in a minute.'

She found Jake at the nurses' station. 'Do you know where Alex is?'

'Talking to painters and choosing nursery furniture with Jo—why?'

Anne groaned. 'There's this woman. . .'

She filled him in, and, not in the least to her surprise, he was all in favour. 'Great idea—let's have a look at her and make sure all's well, and then I can't see why they shouldn't come in at the end.'

Of course he perched on the bed and chatted to Mr and Mrs Bailey, and found out within about thirty seconds that they had a farm and Mrs Bailey raised goats and sheep and so they were all used to seeing farm animals being born.

'They probably won't find it all that fascinating, actually,' Mrs Bailey said with a laugh.

Jake chuckled. 'OK. Well, looking at you I can't see any problems, and you know your own children and how well you cope with labour and delivery. It's up to you.'

Her face broke into a wide smile. 'Thank you.'

They moved her into the birthing-room and lowered the delivery table so it was more like a bed.

'I'd rather not have you on the floor just in case we have difficulties with the second twin,' Jake explained.

As her labour progressed rapidly to the second stage, it was quite obvious to all of them that she was in perfect control, one of the fortunate few for whom childbirth was the straightforward experience nature had intended.

After a while she looked at them and said, 'I think the children should come in now.'

Mr Bailey went and found them, and they stood round in an expectant little semicircle, their eyes like saucers.

'Will you tie ropes on their feet and pull them out like the vet does with the lambs sometimes?' the middle child, a boy, asked.

Jake managed to keep his face straight. 'We don't usually. We have special tongs called forceps for babies that find it harder to be born, but I don't think we'll need them for your mum.'

'I was borned at home,' the smallest one said importantly.

'By accident,' her father said drily, and everyone chuckled.

Anne was keeping her eye on Mrs Bailey, and as the next contraction came her husband propped her up and she pushed down firmly. Almost instantly the first baby's head crowned.

'Here it comes,' said the oldest boy with only the faintest tinge of patronage.

They shuffled closer.

'Pant,' the midwife instructed unnecessarily. Anne began to feel the family could have managed the entire event without them. Within seconds, the first baby was safely delivered and was laid, squalling, in Mrs Bailey's arms.

'Oh, yuck, a girl!' the middle one said.

'Goody!' the youngest one said with a huge grin.

'Well done, Mum,' the oldest said, and Anne could have sworn she saw a tear on his cheek.

Within three minutes the other twin, also a girl, made her appearance without any difficulties at all.

'*Two* girls?' the middle one wailed.

'Shut up, Michael,' his big brother said. 'At least they're healthy!'

The babies were indeed healthy, and in full voice.

Overcoming his distaste, Michael leant over and inspected his little sisters with interest.

'They're all screwed up—can I hold one?'

'Me too!' the littlest put in excitedly.

'Stephen, perhaps you'd supervise to make sure they don't drop them,' their mother said, playing the conciliator automatically.

The children were seated on the couch in the corner and Stephen was handed the babies one at a time to give to his brother and sister to hold. While the medical team hovered anxiously and Anne wondered what their insurance position would be if one of the babies was dropped, the Bailey family quietly got on with the business of getting to know their new members.

'I quite envy Mrs Bailey. No sutures, no drugs—amazing,' Anne said later when they had put Beth to bed and were clearing up in the kitchen.

'Amazing family,' Jake said. 'I wonder how Beth would cope with a brother or sister?'

Anne stopped with her hands in the hot water and turned to him. 'Jake, I—I'm not having any more children, ever.'

He picked up a plate and dried it, watching her, his face gently concerned. 'Was it really so bad?'

She nodded slightly. 'Horrendous. I couldn't do it.'

'Not even with an elective Caesarean section?'

'I thought I was going to die.'

'That was bad management, Annie. I wouldn't let you die, or suffer, come to that.'

'What about Lizzi Hamilton?' she said doubtfully.

He shook his head. 'She didn't suffer that much. It was jolly hard work, but in fact it was a very good delivery.'

She handed him another plate. 'Her baby was all squashed.'

'Babies are often squashed—that's why their bones are so soft. Beth is fine—even with the mismanagement she came to no harm. If you wanted another child, you needn't be afraid. I'd take care of you, Annie.'

She looked into his gentle deep brown eyes, and saw only reassurance. 'Would it matter to you very much if I didn't want any more?'

He shook his head slowly. 'Not really. I love children, and I'd be quite happy with dozens, but they aren't the be-all and end-all for me. If you really felt you couldn't face it, I wouldn't try to persuade you.'

Suddenly she felt the first ray of hope since she had

agreed to marry him. Perhaps in time she might reconsider having another child, but to know he wouldn't push meant an awful lot.

'Thank you, Jake,' she said a little unevenly. 'I was worrying about that.'

'Is that all?'

She looked at him in surprise. 'All?'

He shrugged with forced casualness. 'No doubts, second thoughts?'

He was holding himself rigid, she noted almost absently, as if he dreaded the answer—but what did he want her to say? Was he looking for a way out already?

She took a deep breath and met his eyes. 'No, no second thoughts—for Beth's sake, we have to go through with it.'

Something flickered in his eyes, but it was gone before she could read it.

'Fine.' He turned away and put down the last plate. 'I'm finished now at the hospital until I take over when Jo leaves, so I thought I'd go down to my parents' for a couple of days. Is that OK?'

She nodded numbly. 'Of course. I'll see you on Saturday morning.'

He gave a strained smile. 'I'll ring you. Take care.'

His lips brushed her cheek and he let himself out. Half an hour later she heard him drive away, and when she went to bed she was desperately conscious of the silence from next door.

The next time she saw him would be the wedding, and the next time she heard him getting ready for bed it would be with her.

She wasn't at all sure she could cope with it.

CHAPTER TEN

MATTHEW GABRIEL was troubled.

He stood in his study and gazed sightlessly down the garden. His darling girl, the apple of his eye, was getting married today to a man he couldn't approve of. She assured him that she loved the fellow and that she was just as responsible as him for the birth of their delightful daughter, but Matthew couldn't agree.

Had the man been less of a rake, Matthew might have forgiven him—even encouraged Anne to marry him all those years ago. But she had said quite definitely that he was not the marrying kind, and Matthew had had great hopes of his partner's son Duncan.

In the end, of course, she had married neither of them—not Duncan, becuase she simply refused quite kindly but firmly to do so, and not Jake—perhaps because a meddlesome old man had interfered.

He took a key out of his pocket and, unlocking the little drawer at the back of the bureau, he opened it. In the bottom lay two envelopes addressed to his daughter. He was well aware of the contents—he had read them both when he had seen the return address on the back. At the time, it had seemed like the right thing to do, but now. . .

'Matthew? Darling, come on, we'll be late!'

'Coming, dear.'

He picked up the two letters and slipped them into his pocket, locked the drawer and pocketed the key.

* * *

Anne drew a deep breath. Everyone was in the chapel waiting for her, but she just felt she needed a second more to calm her nerves.

Her doubts were clamouring for her attention. What if he didn't love her? What if she couldn't hold him? What if he changed his mind halfway through and walked out?

She took another steadying breath and gave her father an unsteady smile.

He looked troubled, she thought. Well, he had doubts too.

He coughed slightly and ran his finger round his collar. 'Anne, are you sure about this?'

'No,' she replied quietly. 'If I knew beyond doubt that he loved me, then I'd be sure, but as it is. . .' She lifted her shoulders expressively. 'All I know is that for better or worse, I love him. I just hope that's enough.'

Her father slipped his hand into his pocket and withdrew two crumpled envelopes.

'Seven years ago,' he said gruffly, 'I did an unforgivable thing. It might well have ruined your lives, but fate has given me a chance to put things right. I just pray it's not too late.'

Puzzled, Anne took the letters from him. 'They're from Jake,' she said in bewilderment. She looked at the postmarks. One was dated August, when she had just realised she was pregnant, and the other was the following June.

She raised her eyes and looked at her father in confusion. 'Why didn't I get them?'

'Because at the time I thought there was a possibility you would marry Duncan. You'd made your opinion of Jake perfectly clear, and I didn't want you tied to a man who didn't have it in him to be faithful to you. I opened the first letter, and decided you'd be better off without it. When the second came, I was very much afraid you might do as he suggested, and I didn't want to lose you. I can see now that I was wrong. I can't expect you to forgive me. All I can hope is that it's not too late for you to put things right.'

She looked back down at the letters. Her fingers shaking, she opened the first. It read,

Annie, darling, I'm just back from France, having spent the past two months trying to forget you. It didn't work. Thoughts of you have been with me day and night since I last saw you. I know I said it needn't make any difference, but it has. I can't put you out of my mind, I miss you endlessly, and all I want is to be with you.

You're going to say I'm not the marrying kind, and you may be right, but all I know is I need you with me.

If I don't hear from you, I won't pester you but assume you'll marry Duncan as planned. Whatever, I wanted you to know that I love you.

Jake.

Anne was stunned. She pushed the letter back into the envelope and opened the other. She read,

Darling Annie,
I gather from Jo that you aren't getting married to Duncan after all. When I didn't hear from you before, I assumed you were carrying on as planned, but obviously something has gone wrong.

I don't know if that means there is any hope for me. I still love you, and if you would marry me I would do everything in my power to make you happy.

Jo tells me you have a beautiful baby daughter

called Beth. I would be only too happy to help you look after her and to love her as if she were my own. Who knows? Perhaps in time you could both grow to love me.

I have been offered a job at Guy's, but there is a possibility I might go to New York instead. It all depends on you, and your decision.

Hope to hear from you soon. All my love as always,

Jake.

Anne raised her eyes slowly to her father's unhappy face.

'He wanted to marry me,' she said unsteadily. 'He wanted to marry me and you—Pop, you had no right, just as I had no right to keep his daughter from him.'

'Anne, I——'

She shook her head, quelling the little spurt of anger. 'Don't—not now. We'll talk about it another time. I think I've kept Jake waiting long enough.'

She turned round to where Beth was standing with Jo.

'Ready?' Jo asked her, scanning her face worriedly.

Anne nodded. 'Yes, I'm ready.'

She folded the letters, tucked them into her bodice and took the flowers from Beth.

'All right, darling?'

Beth nodded vigorously, her eyes dancing. Anne smiled and hugged her, then turned back to her father, laying her hand on his arm.

Jo signalled to the organist and slipped into her seat next to Alex, and Anne started down the aisle towards Jake, Beth behind her almost skipping with excitement.

Anne knew how she felt.

As she drew nearer, Jake turned towards her and smiled encouragingly.

Unaware of the tears streaming down her cheeks, she smiled back at him and hurried the last few steps to his side.

Ignoring the entire congregation, he lifted his hand and cupped her cheek, and his thumb brushed away a tear.

'Are you all right?'

She nodded. 'I love you,' she said softly.

His face registered the whole range of emotions from joy to disbelief, and then he laughed with relief and tugged her into his arms.

'God, woman, you pick the damnedest times!' he said unsteadily, and claimed her mouth in a searing kiss that had the congregation drawing its collective breath. Releasing her, he turned back to the chaplain, still smiling broadly. 'Sorry about that,' he said unrepentantly.

'So I see,' he said drily, and winked, then, lifting his arms to embrace the entire gathering, he began, 'Dearly beloved, we are gathered together here. . .'

Jake closed the door of the honeymoon suite behind the porter, and drew Annie into his arms with a sigh of relief.

'I've been dying to hold you for hours,' he murmured.

She rested her head on his shoulder and smiled with contentment. It had been a beautiful wedding, and the reception at Jo's and Alex's had struck just the right note, but it was wonderful to be alone at last.

'Why were you crying when you came down the aisle?' he asked after a moment.

She eased away from him, reached inside the neckline of her suit jacket and retrieved the letters. 'My father gave them to me just before the service,' she said quietly. 'I'd just read them for the first time.'

He gazed at them for a second, then took them from her and laid them carefully on the bedside table.

'You never got them?'

She shook her head.

'Would you have married me then if you had?'

'I don't know—maybe. Quite possibly. And maybe we would have been divorced by now. Who knows?'

He led her to the edge of the bed and sat down, still holding her hand. 'So you never knew I loved you?'

She shook her head. 'No—no, I never knew. I loved you, of course—I had done from the moment I set eyes on you. I thought I was going to die when I watched you drive away that day.'

'It was the hardest thing I've ever done, but I had to let you go. You were going to marry Duncan——'

She shook her head. 'No, I wasn't. I was never engaged to him, I just pretended.'

Jake stared at her in disbelief. 'But why?'

She lifted her shoulders slightly. 'It seemed like a good idea at the time. I'd been in love with you for—oh, years, and things with Duncan had been getting worse and worse. When I went home that summer, I told him there was no point in continuing our relationship. Then I had to face coming back and watching you with all the girls, and I thought, if I pretended to be engaged, nobody would think it was odd if we were seen together, and I could spend as much time with you as I wanted. No one would link our names romantically and we wouldn't have the embarrassment of having to explain that there wasn't anything between us.'

'But there was—or there could have been. Oh, God,

Annie—I could have killed myself when you came back and you were engaged to him. I didn't know how to look at you without begging you to leave him for me——'

He broke off, the hurt clearly visible on his face.

'I thought you didn't care any more,' Anne told him. 'You hardly spoke to me—I was so lonely for you. I'd had this wonderful idea so that we could be together, and then. . . Night after night you were out, a different girl every time—I was so jealous.'

He gave her a wry smile. 'You were meant to be. There were no girls—not that I slept with. I dossed on friends' floors and slept in the car and crept in quietly at four in the morning when your light was off, but it didn't work. You stayed engaged to Duncan——'

'In self-defence.'

'And then I got you pregnant, and your father hung on to my letters and you thought I didn't even care enough to write to you. Oh, God, Annie, what a mess.'

She nodded. 'I'm sorry—especially for not telling you about Beth. That was wrong of me, but at the time. . .'

Her face crumpled. 'All those wasted years. . .'

'Oh, darling, don't.' His arms opened and he cradled her hard against his chest. After a moment she straightened and brushed the tears from her cheeks.

'I'm soaking your jacket,' she said unsteadily.

'To hell with my jacket.' He stood up and pulled her gently to her feet. 'You looked beautiful today, smiling at me through your tears. I've never loved you so much as I did at that moment.'

'Oh, Jake. . .'

'Let me make love to you, Annie. Let me show you how I feel.'

He reached for her and drew her gently into his

arms, just simply holding her for a while until she relaxed against him, then he released her and teased open the buttons on her jacket. As he reached the fine silk and lace underwear that was all she wore, his mouth curved into a lazy, sexy smile.

'I wondered what you had on under it,' he murmured huskily. His finger traced the line of the lace as it dipped over her breasts. 'Beautiful—so soft and feminine.'

His eyes glittering with passion, he eased the jacket off her shoulders, throwing it over a chair. Her skirt followed, then he lifted her and laid her on the bed, removing her shoes and then slowly, unhurriedly rolling down her stockings and slipping them over her feet. He was standing by the bed and she lay there, watching him as he undressed her.

'Are you going to wear that suit all night?' she asked him innocently.

'Not if you take it off me.'

She swallowed. He reminded her of a panther, sleek and graceful, watchful, controlled. She had never seen him lose control totally, and a little part of her wondered rather bravely what it would be like to unleash the real Jake Hunter.

Before many seconds had passed, she found out.

Kneeling up, she eased his tie around his neck, pulling the end free and throwing it over the end of the bed. The jacket followed, then the shirt. As she reached for the zip of his trousers, his breathing became jerky and his eyes were heavy-lidded and almost black with passion.

As she eased the last of his clothes from his body, the remaining fragment of control deserted him. With a ragged groan he reached out for her, one hand cupping her bottom and holding her hard against him as the other hand cradled her head to steady it under the onslaught of his mouth.

Her blood was racing, her heart hammering against her ribs, and she writhed against him, murmuring incoherent words against his lips.

His fingers found the tiny buttons on her underwear and unfastened them with astonishing ease, then with a massive effort he controlled himself again and lifted his head.

'Are you protected? I don't want to get you pregnant by mistake.'

If she had still doubted his love, that thoughtfulness would have proved it to her beyond any doubt.

'It's OK,' she whispered, and a tiny part of her was sad that it was so. 'I want you, Jake—please, now. . .'

That was the last she saw of his control. He was wild and untamed, voracious, magnificent in his need, demanding her response and glorying in it, and, as the world shattered into stardust all around them, he was there for her, with her, holding her hard against his chest, her name a savage cry of triumph on his lips.

'I love you,' she whispered later.

'I know. I still can't really believe it. I've been so scared for the past few weeks that you were marrying me just for Beth's sake. I tried to tell myself that if I was gentle and patient with you, perhaps you'd grow to love me, but I was so afraid that if you hadn't come to love me in twelve years then nothing I could do now would change that.' He pressed his lips to her hair. 'The other day I thought you were going to change your mind.'

She shook her head. 'I thought you were. You seemed so distant.'

He laughed softly. 'I've been avoiding you because I

didn't trust myself around you. I think I've nearly driven Jo and Alex mad, I've spent so much time with them. I wanted you so badly, and I didn't want you to think I was just marrying you for sex.'

'It might have helped me. I didn't know where you were. I thought you weren't interested in me, and I managed to convince myself you were using me to get Beth.'

He shook his head. 'No—rather the other way round. I was using Beth as a lever to persuade you to marry me, but just recently I've been wondering if it was such a smart move. I'm not sure how I would have coped with living with you without your love. I've had one loveless marriage; the thought of another was terrifying.'

'Tell me about it.'

'My marriage? There's not much to tell. She was a nice enough girl, pretty, friendly, educated. We would have been quite well suited if we'd loved each other, but we didn't—at least, not enough to make it work.

'It was OK at first. It was good to have someone to come home to and share things with, and we got on fairly well, I suppose. Our main problem was sex. It was OK to start with, but after a while I found myself shutting my eyes and pretending she was you, but she didn't feel the same and she didn't sound the same, and after a bit she told me she couldn't be the girl I wanted her to be. We split up then, and her solicitor talked her into a massive divorce claim. I worked my butt off to get some savings behind me, then I left New York and came back here to enrol for my FRCS exams because I couldn't get the sort of job I wanted with my American qualifications. In between studying and some locum work in London, I went to Romania—the rest you know.'

'Do you ever hear from her?'

'Laurel? No.'

'Pretty name.'

He smiled. 'Pretty girl, but she couldn't turn my heart inside out and tie my tongue in knots and make my legs go weak.'

Anne giggled. 'That sounds terribly messy! Do I really do all that to you?'

'You know you do,' he laughed, and hugged her close, suddenly serious. 'Oh, God, Annie, it's been so long—so many long, lonely years without you. I've missed you every day.'

'I've missed you, too. I'm so sorry. It was all so unnecessary—if we'd only been honest with each other about our feelings. . .'

'We must be honest now—even if it hurts. I don't want any more secrets between us, ever.'

She turned on her side and snuggled closer to him. 'There's been something I've been meaning to ask you. I don't know if I'm going to like the answer, but I need to know.'

He twisted his head round and peered at her. 'What is it?'

'It's about Romania.' She twiddled the tip of her finger round his chest hair absently. 'Will you be going back?'

He sighed. 'I don't know. I doubt it. For a start it's expensive—I spent nearly all my savings supporting myself for the past couple of years. For another thing it's very emotionally demanding, and you can only do so much before you either get hardened or crack up. Anyway, I've got you and Beth to look after now. I've missed enough of you, God knows I don't want to miss any more.'

'Was that a no?'

He chuckled. 'I think so. Certainly for the next couple of years. I might do the odd bit of fundraising or campaigning, but that's all. Now I've got a wife and child, I need to get myself on to this career ladder and get stuck into some meteoric progress.'

She smiled and, lifting her hand, she smoothed his rough jaw. 'I'm very proud of what you did for the Romanian hospital, but I'm terribly glad you aren't planning to go back. I need you, like the desert needs rain. Even though I had Beth, my life was empty without you.'

'Not any more,' he whispered, and wrapped her firmly in his arms. 'Now I've got you, I'm never going to let you go again.'

'Good.' With a smile of contentment, she snuggled down against him and fell asleep, safe in the shelter of his arms.

AUTHOR'S NOTE

THE overthrow of the Ceauçescu regime brought us the moving story of the plight of children in Romanian orphanages, a story that shocked and distressed all those who saw it. Many, like Anneka Rice, were moved to help. Others gave what they could. Professionals have contributed time and skills, but still it goes on.

Although Jake Hunter and the hospital in which he worked in Romania are completely fictitious, Barbara Butler, her charity Romaniaid and the orphanage at Goesti are all very real. By the time you read this, Romaniaid will have completed the replumbing and refurbishment of the paediatric ward at Tirgu Frumos, the nearest hospital to the orphanage, and the volunteers will still be running the orphanage.

This is by no means the only organisation helping the Romanian people to get back on their feet. You may know of one near you. If so, don't let the television pictures make you immune to the level of suffering. It's so easy to get used to it and to forget, but the cost of this book would buy formula for a Romanian baby for about ten days. It isn't much to make so much difference.

By buying this book you have already helped. If you want to do more, you can contact Barbara Butler at the following address: High View, Tuddenham Lane, Witnesham, IPSWICH IP6 9HL, or contact your own local charity.

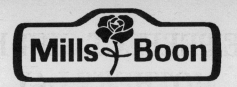

Mills & Boon

Discover the thrill of 4 Exciting Medical Romances – FREE

FREE
BOOKS FOR YOU

In the exciting world of modern
medicine, the emotions of true love
have an added drama. Now you can
experience four of these
unforgettable romantic tales of passion
and heartbreak FREE – and look forward to
a regular supply of Mills & Boon
Medical Romances delivered direct to your door!

🐾 🐾 🐾

Turn the page for details of 2 extra
free gifts, and how to apply.

An Irresistible Offer from Mills & Boon

Here's an offer from Mills & Boon to become a regular reader of Medical Romances. To welcome you, we'd like you to have four books, a cuddly teddy and a special MYSTERY GIFT, all absolutely free and without obligation.

Then, every month you could look forward to receiving 4 more **brand new** Medical Romances for £1.70 each, delivered direct to your door, post and packing free. Plus our newsletter featuring author news, competitions, special offers, and lots more.

This invitation comes with no strings attached. You can cancel or suspend your subscription at any time, and still keep your free books and gifts.

Its so easy. Send no money now. Simply fill in the coupon below and post it at once to -

Mills & Boon Reader Service, FREEPOST, PO Box 236, Croydon, Surrey CR9 9EL

NO STAMP REQUIRED
